
MENTAL HEALTH AND SOCIAL MEDICINE DIVISION
General Editor H. L. FREEMAN

Behavior Therapy Techniques

A GUIDE TO THE TREATMENT OF NEUROSES

From the standpoint of process, there is not the slightest difference between an actual impression with its sequels, and the memory of the impression.

(SECHENOV, *Reflexes of the Brain*, 1863)

If a conscious psychical act is not accompanied by any external manifestations, it still remains a reflex.

(SECHENOV, *Reflexes of the Brain*, 1863)

Timidity will always diminish if the occasions that produce it be skilfully repeated.

(YORITOMO-TASHI, 12th Century)

Behavior Therapy Techniques

A GUIDE TO THE TREATMENT OF NEUROSES

by

JOSEPH WOLPE, M.D.
Professor of Psychiatry, Temple University School of Medicine
Philadelphia, Pennsylvania

AND

ARNOLD A. LAZARUS, P.H.D.
Director, Behavior Therapy Institute, Sausalito, California

PERGAMON PRESS
OXFORD · LONDON · EDINBURGH · NEW YORK
TORONTO · PARIS · BRAUNSCHWEIG

Pergamon Press Ltd., Headington Hill Hall, Oxford
4 & 5 Fitzroy Square, London W.1

Pergamon Press (Scotland) Ltd., 2 & 3 Teviot Place, Edinburgh 1

Pergamon Press Inc., 44–01 21st Street, Long Island City, New York 11101

Pergamon of Canada, Ltd., 6 Adelaide Street East, Toronto, Ontario

Pergamon Press S.A.R.L., 24 rue des Écoles, Paris 5e

Vieweg & Sohn GmbH, Burgplatz 1, Braunschweig

First edition 1966

Library of Congress Catalog Card No. 66–18405

Printed in the United States of America
1967

(2761/66)

Contents

PREFACE vii

Chapter 1. Introduction 1

2. Basic Principles for the Practice of Behavior Therapy 12

3. The Gathering of Data and the Selection of Techniques 24

4. Assertive Training 38

5. Systematic Desensitization 54

6. The Use of Sexual Responses 102

7. Drugs, Carbon Dioxide and Abreaction 116

8. Additional Techniques 130

9. The Results of Behavior Therapy 154

Appendix 1. Life History Questionnaire 165

2. Personality Schedule 170

3. Fear Inventory 172

4. Relaxation Techniques 177

BIBLIOGRAPHY 181

AUTHOR INDEX 189

SUBJECT INDEX 193

Preface

ALTHOUGH the techniques of habit change that Lazarus (1958) christened "behavior therapy" have been adopted by an ever-increasing circle of psychotherapists during more than a decade, there is still no institution anywhere in the world where a systematic schooling in their theory and practice can be obtained. Even if this situation were soon to change, the number and distribution of facilities would obviously be limited for some years; so that, as in the past, the learning of behavior therapy will continue to a great extent to have a "do-it-yourself" character. The most important function of this small volume should be to facilitate the process of self-education; but we hope it will also be of use to those fortunate enough to have personal instruction as well.

The most widely used behavior therapy techniques continue to be those given prominence in Wolpe's *Psychotherapy by Reciprocal Inhibition*, and we have therefore given special attention to them. In addition, we have described certain recent modifications, as well as some new techniques, which, though only at an early stage of investigation, promise to be valuable additions to the armamentarium. We have not tried to encompass the full range of techniques available to the behavior therapist. The explicit use of positive reinforcement and its corollaries is only mentioned in passing. Again, details of the manipulation of environmental events and other operant conditioning strategies have been omitted. Most clinicians do not have access to the highly controlled environments that are essential for the effective application of most operant conditioning methods. Also omitted are some ingenious procedures that are either extremely time-consuming or require the construction of expensive apparatus.

The effective utilization of most of the techniques described in this book does not require medical training, but medical screening of cases to be treated by non-medical therapists is necessary in order to exclude organic problems which masquerade as neuroses. The conventional training obtained in most graduate courses in clinical psychology, with their emphasis on Freudian theories and projective testing, is largely irrelevant to the practice of behavior therapy and often proves to be a positive hindrance. On the other hand, to read this book so as to obtain an adequate understanding of the techniques described is scarcely possible, unless the student has satisfied two minimum prerequisites. First, he should have a reasonable grounding in essential scientific methodology (e.g. Popper, 1956, 1962). Second, he should have acquired a knowledge of modern learning theory (especially Hull, 1943 and Skinner, 1953), and an acquantance with the developments which have taken place during the past few years (e.g. Mowrer, 1960; Kimble, 1961; Razran, 1961; Bandura and Walters, 1963.)

As time goes on a progressively more receptive attitude is developing towards behavior therapy in the psychiatric professions. The reactions of psychoanalysts and their followers have shown an interesting succession of changes. The initial reaction was one of benevolent amusement at the "naive", "superficial", and "mechanistic" procedures which would "obviously" result in rapid relapse, symptom substitution, or generally augmented anxiety since the repressed roots of the problem remained unresolved. When these dire predictions failed to materialize, "extension of time" was the excuse for continuing forebodings. We were informed that the inevitable relapses or development of new symptoms might take many months, perhaps years, to develop. When Wolpe (1958) followed up several patients as long as 7 years after they had been treated by him, and found that they had either maintained improvement or improved further without additional therapy, the typical reaction was a dismissal of the results as "transference cures", "mere ego strengthening", or "fortuitous sampling" (e.g. Glover, 1959). Others were inclined to impugn the entire issue by asserting that

Wolpe's results had no bearing on his theories but were due entirely to his "therapeutic personality". This particular maneuver collapsed under the impact of independent corroborative reports which revealed that therapists employing these techniques achieved similar results despite wide divergence in their personalities (see Eysenck, 1960). Recently the opposition's trend has been to accept the value of behavior therapeutic techniques but to claim that they are effective for only a limited range of conditions and due to psychoanalytic "mechanisms".

We venture to predict that before long there will be a retreat from this position also. It is, in the first place, somewhat ludicrous to ascribe the effects of behavior therapy to psychoanalytic mechanisms when the efficacy of these has not even been demonstrated (i.e. *tested and upheld by observation*, not "interpreted") in the context of psychoanalytic therapy itself. Second, controlled comparative studies (e.g. Lazarus, 1961; Paul, 1966) have so far consistently found behavior therapy significantly more effective than interpretative methods. Third, in certain instances (Wolpe, 1963) therapeutic change has been shown to be quantitatively related to the amount of defined therapeutic activity. Fourth, time spent in therapy is relatively brief, often strikingly so. Finally, there is the general consideration that if, as all agree, neuroses are determined by experiences, their basis must be learning; and what can be a more appropriate instrument for overcoming them than a knowledge of the laws of learning?

We are grateful to Mr. L. J. Lazarus, Dr. James Anker and Dr. Peter Bentler for their constructive criticisms of several chapters.

CHAPTER 1

Introduction

A HABIT is a consistent way of responding to defined stimulus conditions. Ordinarily, a habit declines—undergoes extinction—when its consequences become unadaptive, i.e. when it fails either to subserve the needs of the organism or to avoid injury, pain or fatigue. Neurotic habits are distinguished by their resistance to extinction in the face of their unadaptiveness.[1] Behavior therapy is the application of experimentally established principles of learning to the overcoming of these persistent habits. In order to change a habit it is always necessary to modify the individual responses that constitute it. Change thus depends on eliciting behavior that can modify these individual responses.

Historical Perspective

While the modern behavior therapist deliberately applies principles of learning to his therapeutic operations, empirical behavior therapy is probably as old as civilization—if we consider civilization as having begun when man first did things to further the well-being of other men. From the time that this became a feature of human life there must have been occasions when a man complained of his ills to another who advised or persuaded him on a course of action. In a broad sense, this could be called behavior therapy whenever the behavior itself was conceived as the therapeutic agent.

Ancient writings contain innumerable behavioral prescriptions that accord with this broad conception of behavior therapy. It

[1] For a detailed discussion see Wolpe (1958).

is irrelevant whether the methods worked or not, but a good many of them undoubtedly did work at times. Often, surely, there were "suggestion" effects or "placebo" effects, by virtue of the responses to which words or things had previously been conditioned; and sometimes the instigated changes in behavior would have led to reconditioning, with beneficial consequences for emotionally disturbed states.

Despite the derogation he usually receives, Mesmer (1779) deserves our salutation as perhaps the first therapist to base his efforts at behavior change on a general behavioral principle. Although that principle did not stand up to scientific testing it generated procedures that *were* often successful. Their essential elements were subsequently elucidated by the researches of de Puysegur, Bernheim and later investigators, and were the fountainhead of later techniques of suggestion and hypnosis (and other forms of verbal control of behavior) which have continued to play a part in behavior therapy—and probably always will.

The classical forms of suggestion are designed to substitute desirable for undesirable behavior by direct verbal prescription. It now seems that when this works it is because the new response competes with the old, and, if it dominates, inhibits the latter. Whenever, either immediately or after repetition, this is followed by lasting diminution (or elimination) of the old response we have an instance of conditioned inhibition based on reciprocal inhibition (see below). Unfortunately, it does not work very often.

An early example of a less direct use of competing responses that is remarkably close to some modern practices was recently unearthed by Stewart (1961) in a book by Leuret (1846). The patient was a 30-year-old wine merchant with a 10-year history of obsessional thoughts which had become so insistent that he had ceased to be able to carry on his business. Having admitted the patient to hospital, Leuret ordered him to read and learn songs which he could recite the next day. The patient's food ration depended upon how much he had learnt. This regime continued for about 6 weeks during which the patient's recitals steadily improved. Meanwhile, his obsessional thoughts were interfering less and less, and at the end of the 6 weeks he told Leuret that he had not had the thoughts for several days and that he felt much better. Leuret found him work as a nurse, and a year later noted that he was still well and a very successful nurse.

The nineteenth-century therapist had some empirical guidelines for his techniques, but each therapeutic foray was an experiment whose outcome could not be predicted. The arrival on the scene of Sigmund Freud led to the appearance of a new group of techniques that were based on coherent theoretical principles. These may be regarded as constituting a more systematic attempt at behavior therapy for it was through behavior that these techniques sought to accomplish the therapeutic aim. They did not, in fact, afford the hoped-for increase in favorable and predictable outcomes, but they fascinated the mind because they were set in a remarkably ingenious and colorful theoretical framework, and stimulated tremendous interest in problems of human behavior.

Nevertheless, during the first half of the twentieth century, in terms of scientific advancement, no other field of knowledge lay more stagnant than behavioral therapeutics. No hypotheses were being put to the test; no lawful relations were being established; and no reliable rules existed for effecting therapeutic change. The explanation for this is simple. All therapy is applied science; and behavior therapy could not enter the world of science before there was a sufficient foundation for it in the basic studies of the experimental laboratory. Psychotherapy stands in the same relation to behavior science (psychology) as medicine to physiology. Because physiology established lawful relations earlier than behavioral science did, medicine could advance on a scientific footing before psychotherapy could.

The Development of Scientific Behavior Therapy

Eventually, as studies of normal behavior, which took place largely in the laboratory, revealed more and more about the factors determining the acquisition, elicitation, maintenance, and decline of habits, some of this knowledge lent itself to the construction of hypotheses to account for the special characteristics of certain types of abnormal behavior. Certain of these hypotheses subsequently withstood observations that tested them, thereby acquiring scientific standing.

The most-studied habit-eliminating process is experimental extinction—the gradual decrement in strength and frequency of responses that follows their unreinforced evocation. Three decades ago Dunlap (1932) probed the therapeutic possibilities of this process, and evolved the technique called "negative practice", whereby undesirable motor habits are overcome through securing their repeated evocation. About the same time, Guthrie observed the general therapeutic applicability of the idea of counterconditioning, stating that the simplest rule for breaking a habit is "to find the cues that initiate the action and to practice another response to these cues" (Guthrie, 1935, p. 138). He stressed the need to control the situation so that the cue to the original response is present while "other behavior prevails".

The next step forward was the application of Guthrie's principle to the experimental neurosis, which had first been produced in Pavlov's laboratories early in the twentieth century, and many times subsequently.[1] But because the behavior of neurotic animals is strikingly different from normal, and is, moreover, exceedingly persistent, all the earlier experimenters shared the opinion that some kind of lesion or physiopathology was the basis of the neuroses. The Russian workers believed this opinion to be supported by the finding that in certain instances the neuroses were overcome by giving the animals depressant or

[1] Some of the following material has been slightly modified from "Psychotherapy: the nonscientific heritage and the new science", Wolpe, J., *Behav. Res. Ther.* **1**:23–8, 1963.

excitant drugs. However, in 1943, grounds for dissent from this view emerged. Masserman, in the course of a fascinating series of experiments on cats that had been made neurotic by being shocked in a small cage, observed that the neuroses could be overcome if the animals could be induced to feed in the experimental cage in which the neurosis had been produced. The fact that the mere evocation of particular patterns of behavior could "cure" the neuroses spoke against a lesion theory, and the fact that in order to procure the change the behavior had to be evoked in the experimental cage (in contrast to the living cage) strongly suggested that learning was at play. It must be said that these were not the conclusions reached by Masserman who, deeply steeped in "psychodynamic" thinking, interpreted the facts in terms of "breaking through the motivational conflict"—a view whose inadequacy was pointed out several years later (Wolpe, 1956).

The next requirement was to devise tests for the learning hypothesis. To begin with it was necessary to define "learning" quite clearly. The following definition was adopted:

> Learning may be said to have occurred if a response has been evoked in temporal contiguity with a given sensory stimulus and it is subsequently found that the stimulus can evoke the response although it could not have done so before. If the stimulus could have evoked the reponse before but subsequently evokes it more strongly, then, too, learning may be said to have occurred. [Wolpe, 1952a.]

Several predictions were then made that would necessarily be fulfilled if the neurotic behavior were indeed learned. If they were not fulfilled the learning hypothesis would have to be abandoned. They were:

1. The behavior manifested in an experimental neurosis must be essentially the same as that elicited by the stimulus situation that precipitates the neurosis.
2. The neurotic behavior must be at greatest intensity when the animal is exposed to stimuli most like those in the presence of which the neurosis was precipitated, and the intensity must decrease as a direct function of diminishing resemblance (according to the principle of primary stimulus generalization).
3. Unlearning of neurotic behavior should occur in circumstances like

those that produce unlearning in other contexts, i.e. extinction and/or counterconditioning.

Each of these predictions was submitted to experimental testing in 1947 (Wolpe, 1952, 1958) in cat neuroses produced by high-voltage, low-amperage shocks in an experimental cage similar to that used by Masserman, and each prediction was sustained. In every animal the features of the reactions to shock were duplicated in the reactions of the neurosis. The intensity of neurotic response decreased as the environment to which the neurotic animal was exposed was less similar to that of the experimental cage. While the reactions could not be overcome by the extinction process (partly, it seems, because of the small amount of reactive inhibition evoked by autonomic responses (cf. Wolpe, 1958)), it was possible to eliminate them through the reciprocal inhibition of weak anxiety responses by feeding. The animals would first be fed in a place where only slight anxiety was aroused—by stimuli remote on a generalization continuum—and when the anxiety had disappeared would be progressively advanced along the continuum (see Chapter 5).

The foregoing having provided some assurance that experimental neuroses were learned, the next proposition that called for testing was that *human* neuroses are parallel to experimental neuroses in respect of the three features at issue: acquisition by learning, primary stimulus generalization and elimination by unlearning.

With regard to the first, a study was made of the historical antecedents of the "symptoms" in clinical cases of neurosis. In a large proportion of them a clear history of the time of onset of particular reactions was obtained. In these instances the patient recalled either a particular occasion of great distress or else the repeated arousal of anxiety in a recurrent situation involving, for example, a threatening parent or a hostile schoolteacher. It was invariably found that neurotic reactions whose origin could be dated to such experiences had come to be evocable by stimuli similar to stimuli that were to the forefront in the precipitating situations (although other stimuli later became effective in many cases, through second-order conditioning) (see Wolpe, 1958).

It was also evident that human neurotic reactions obey the principle of primary stimulus generalization (Wolpe, 1958, 1961a). As in the animal neuroses, their intensity is determined by the degree of similarity of the evoking stimulus to a zenithal stimulus that is often identical with the original conditioned stimulus. In a particular case there may be several physically unrelated classes of anxiety-arousing stimuli, each of which is found on examination to have a zenith and a generalization gradient. The ranked members of a gradient constitute a hierarchy. In man there are often hierarchies based upon similarities of internal effects (secondary generalization)—Osgood's "mediated generalization". For example, physically dissimilar situations may have in common the theme of rejection, and in so far as the patient is disturbed by rejection the situations can be placed in a hierarchical order determined by the relative strength of the reactions they evoke. To take a particular instance in another area (Wolpe, 1961), a case of claustrophobia also had claustrophobic reactions in situations that had the mere "feel" of enclosement, e.g. a tight zipper, or wanting to remove nail-polish while having no access to remover (see Chapter 5).

The third question concerns the role of learning in bringing about recovery. Like animal neuroses, human neuroses are not usually extinguishable by repeated evocation of the neurotic responses, and for the same reasons. The first evidence that they may be overcome by graduated counterconditioning was reported (and then forgotten) as early as 1924, when Mary Cover Jones treated children's phobias by feeding the child in the presence of the fearful object at progressively diminishing distances (see p. 55), a technique almost identical with that used in the animal neuroses mentioned above. In recent years, adult human neuroses have been treated by methods that employ responses other than feeding for the reciprocal inhibition and counterconditioning of anxiety (Wolpe, 1958; Eysenck, 1960), and these are the main subject matter of this book.

The information invoked above to answer the questions regarding human neuroses has been essentially "clinical", but in so far as the observations have been consistent and have been confirmed by independent observers, it may be said that the learning hypothesis of neurosis has cleared its first hurdles and qualified as a scientific hypothesis.

But properly controlled experimental observations are necessary. While a great deal has to be done, some data are already available, and all accord with the clinical findings. Experiments on the *production* of human neuroses are naturally considered with hesitation, if not trepidation, so that it is not surprising that only three are known to us. One is the famous Watson and Rayner experiment (1920), in which little Albert was rendered fearful of furry objects by the loud striking of an iron bar behind him whenever he reached out toward and touched a white rat. The second is Krasnogorski's (1925) induction of experimental neuroses in children by exposing them to ambivalent stimuli in relation to the conditioning of alimentary responses—a procedure very similar to the usual technique for producing experimental neuroses in Pavlov's laboratories (Pavlov, 1927). Finally, Campbell, Sanderson and Laverty (1964) have demonstrated (though not in a context of *neurosis production*) that marked anxiety reactions can be conditioned by a single severe stress due to muscular paralysis, and furthermore, that repeated evocation of the conditioned response is accompanied by increased strength of response, instead of extinction—in keeping with a common clinical experience.

It is much more congenial to perform *therapeutic* experiments, and we look forward to a growing output of process studies in coming years. As an earnest of this promise there has recently been one notable contribution in the counterconditioning field. Lang and Lazovik (1963), Lang (1964), and Lang, Lazovik and Reynolds (1965) in controlled studies of the desensitization of snake phobias have found that therapeutic change is apparently due to the conditioning procedure, and cannot be attributed to suggestion, rapport ("transference") or muscle relaxation. In the field of therapy employing operant conditioning, process studies are already numerous. A considerable number of them have been collected by Ullmann and Krasner (1965).

The Effects of Behavior Therapy

The most distinctive feature of behavior therapy is in the command it gives to the therapist both in planning the general strategy of therapy and controlling its details as he goes along. When one type of maneuver fails to accomplish change, another is tried according to appropriate indications, each variation being an application of an experimentally established principle. When a procedure shows signs of inhibiting the patient's anxiety responses it is systematically applied to whittle away the anxiety-evoking potential of precisely those stimuli in relation to which the therapist chooses to use it. The specificity of effect is often extremely clear, as shown, for example, in an experimental case study (Wolpe, 1962) involving a multifaceted motor car phobia. It has also been shown (Wolpe, 1963) that in the case of classical phobias treated by desensitization therapy, there is a mathematical relationship between the number of scene presentations and the degree of procured recovery. In claustrophobias and other phobias in which fear increases with proximity to a feared object, this is a positively accelerating function, whereas in acrophobias and agoraphobias it is a negatively accelerating function. The curves approximate to simple power functions (p. 90).

The foregoing state of affairs is in strong contrast to the conventional therapist's rather helpless position. In the conditions set for his interactions with the patient, he can only passively hope that some constructive result will emerge in the course of procedures that are stylized and relatively inflexible. He has to rely *solely* on interviewing and interpretative skills.

In the conventional literature on psychotherapy much has consequently been made of the patient–therapist relationship. A widely prevalent belief is that the quality of the therapeutic relationship is more basic to therapeutic outcome than the therapist's specific methods and techniques, and this is probably true of the conventional therapies. As Franks (1961) has shown, a relationship in which the therapist is able to mobilize the patient's expectation of help and hope of relief is in and of itself a powerful therapeutic instrument. But the active implementation of the conditioning procedures described in this book adds to the generalized benefits which accrue when people establish close rapport. The practice of behavior therapy may thus be viewed as a "double-barrelled" means of alleviating neurotic distress. As in most systems of psychotherapy, the patient enjoys the nonjudgmental acceptance of a person whom he perceives as possessing the necessary skills and desire to be of service, but, in behavior therapy he receives, in addition, the benefits of special conditioning procedures which have independent validity.

The charge that it is Machiavellian or antihumanistic to influence and control patients' behavior by deliberate deconditioning procedures falls away when one realizes that all therapists exercise personal control over their patients. Several studies have shown that all therapists control their patients by (at least) rewarding them with approval and interest when they respond in a prescribed manner, whereas when patients behave in ways that threaten the therapist or run counter to his objectives, they are "punished" by means of withdrawal of interest and other subtle forms of disapproval (Bandura *et al.*, 1960; Murray, 1956; Rogers, 1960). Although so-called "nondirective" therapists supposedly avoid the imposition of their own value systems and remain entirely neutral, even patients who improve under reflective therapy tend to revise certain of their values in the direction of their therapist's values (Rosenthal, 1955). An appreciation of the processes of verbal conditioning will clarify why Krasner (1958) maintains that "all psychotherapy is to some extent directive in nature". The transmission of subtle cues which may be deliberate or inadvertent on the therapist's part will tend to guide, control, modify or manipulate patients' behavior. London (1964) has concluded that "either therapists can successfully influence behavior or they cannot, and they have little choice of what to claim. If they wish to say they cannot do so, or may not do so . . . one must ask what right they have to be in business."

Statistical studies of the effects of behavior therapy by competent therapists have shown that a percentage of recoveries or marked improvements that approaches 90 may be expected among patients who have had a reasonable amount of exposure to the available methods. These studies are summarized in Chapter 9, where they are also compared with similar studies on psychoanalytical therapy. The comparisons are extremely favorable to behavior therapy, but vulnerable to the criticism of lack of control. The results of some well-controlled outcome studies, however, also emerge decisively on the side of behavior therapy. A point that must be given the strongest emphasis is that *behavior therapy is effective in all neuroses* and not only in unitary phobias.

All in all, there is reason for confidence in the future of behavior therapy. It is founded in biology and its principles and practices are determined by the rules of science. Its clinical results are encouraging. Yet it is only in its infancy. The methods in use today will look very rough-hewn a decade or two from now. We may anticipate the fulfilment of Reyna's (1964) expectation that "more rigorous applications of the laws of learning will render conditioning therapies even more effective; and will extend their use to a broader range of behavior problems".

CHAPTER 2

Basic Principles for the Practice of Behavior Therapy

Technical Principles

The aim of behavior therapy is always to change habits judged undesirable. The achievement of this aim depends on the application of one or more of three categories of conditioning operations.

1. *Counterconditioning*

A basic premise about neuroses is that they are persistent, unadaptive learned habits of reaction (see Chapter 1). Almost universally, anxiety is a prominent constituent of neurotic reactions; and since anxiety involves a primitive (subcortical) level of neural organization, its unlearning can be procured only through processes that involve this primitive level. Neurotic anxiety cannot be overcome by purely intellectual action—logical argument, rational insight—except in the special case where it stems entirely from misconceptions (see below).

The elimination of anxiety-response habits always seems to require the inhibition of anxiety by a competing response. The formal process is the establishment of conditioned inhibition through what has been called the "reciprocal inhibition principle": *If a response inhibitory of anxiety can be made to occur in the presence of anxiety-evoking stimuli it will weaken the bond between these stimuli and the anxiety.* In human neuroses, a considerable number of responses which empirically inhibit anxiety have been successfully used to overcome neurotic anxiety-response habits as well as other neurotic habits. For example, assertive responses (Chapter 4) are used to overcome neurotic anxieties that inhibit effective action towards those persons with whom the patient has to interact. The essence of the therapist's role is to encourage the outward expression, under all reasonable circumstances, of the feelings and action tendencies previously inhibited by anxiety. Each act of assertion reciprocally inhibits to some extent the concurrent anxiety and slightly weakens the anxiety-response habit. The reduction of anxiety drive is the main reinforcing agent of this habit change. Similarly, relaxation responses can be employed to bring about systematic decrements of anxiety-response patterns to many classes of stimuli (Chapter 5).

The reciprocal inhibition principle also comes into play in overcoming responses other than anxiety. It is the basis of the conditioned inhibition of obsessional and compulsive habits by aversion therapy. In this treatment a painful faradic shock or similar stimulus inhibits the evocation of the undesired behavior with the result that some conditioned inhibition of the latter is procured and built up by repetition (Chapter 8). There are also many instances of positive conditioning which *ipso facto* include the conditioned inhibition of previous habits of response to the antecedent stimuli concerned. For example, when assertive behavior is instigated, while the expression of "positive" feelings produces conditioned inhibition of anxiety, the motor actions involved in such expression inhibit and consequently displace the previous motor habit. It should be noted that here the reinforcement comprises the various "rewarding" consequences of the new response (Chapter 4).

2. *Positive Reconditioning*

The conditioning of new motor habits or ways of thinking may be part and parcel of the overcoming of unadaptive autonomic responses, as in the example just given. But frequently, new habits of action or thought are needed in contexts that do not involve anxiety. An instance of this is the conditioning treatment of enuresis nocturna. By arranging for the patient to be awakened by an alarm as soon as the first drop of urine is excreted during sleep, the waking reaction is conditioned to the imminence of urination, and this subsequently leads to the development of an inhibition of the tendency to urinate in response to bladder stimulation during sleep (H. G. Jones, 1960; Lovibond, 1963). A further example is the conditioning of effective study habits in individuals who have previously developed unproductive habits that fritter away their time in the setting where they should be working.

Successful conditioning in such examples as the latter always involves the use of "reward" of one kind or another. It often suffices to apply these on an *ad hoc* basis, but in recent years there has been increasing systematic use of Skinner's (1953) operant conditioning techniques to remove and replace undesirable habits. The essence of this approach is to elicit a new behavior pattern in the relevant situation, by rewarding each desired response, while consistently not rewarding, or even punishing, any undesired behavior. For example, anorexia nervosa has been successfully treated by making social rewards such as the use of a radio or the granting of companionship contingent on eating, withdrawing these rewards when the patient fails to eat (Bachrach, Erwin and Mohr, 1965). Various schizophrenic and psychopathic cases have been treated on the same principle (Lindsley, 1956), Ayllon, 1963; Williams, 1959; Davison, 1964) and major and lasting changes of behavior have been procured, even in patients who have been hospitalized for 10–30 years. This approach promises to yield many methods for controlling psychopathological behavior patterns.

3. *Experimental Extinction*

This is the progressive weakening of a habit through the repeated nonreinforcement of the responses that manifest it. Thus behavior that has been established by food reinforcement becomes progressively weaker if its occurrences are not followed by food. The same is usually true of avoidance behavior if it is not reinforced by an occasional shock. The very evocation of the response has effects that are self-weakening, whether or not it should ultimately be proved that this depends on the fatigue-associated reactive inhibition mechanism proposed by Hull (1943).

Therapeutic techniques based on the extinction mechanism, introduced a quarter of a century ago by Dunlap (1932) under the name "negative practice", have in recent years again been employed in the treatment of such motor habits as tics (e.g. Yates, 1958). It is found that in correlation with a very large number of unreinforced deliberate evocations of it, spontaneous evocations of the undesired movement are progressively lessened.

There are certain therapeutic maneuvers that superficially *appear* to apply the extinction principle to the elimination of emotional reactions (e.g. Malleson, 1959; Frankl, 1960). These involve exposing the patient to anxiety-arousing stimuli, either in reality or in imagination *at the greatest possible strength.* There is no doubt that in some cases this leads to the decline and ultimate elimination of the anxiety response habit, but in our experience it more often does not. In some cases it may produce severe intensification of a phobia, which is then more difficult to eradicate by other means. The use of such techniques is seriously limited by our inability to predict which patients are likely to benefit and which are not. There is, in any case, good reason to doubt that the mechanism involved is really experimental extinction when the evocation of high anxiety is followed by improvement. It has been evident, both clinically (Wolpe, 1958) and experimentally (Campbell *et al.*, 1964), that the elicitation of a high intensity anxiety response *increases* rather than decreases the habit strength of that response. Part of the explanation for this may be that autonomic responses do not yield much of the fatigue-associated reactive inhibition that is assumed to be the basis of extinction (Hull, 1943). Furthermore, any extinctive tendency is countered by the drive reduction (reinforcement) that follows cessation of, or removal from, the anxiety-arousing stimulation (Wolpe, 1958) (see also Chapter 8).

TACTICAL PRINCIPLES

An explicit assumption of the behavior therapist is that human behavior is subject to causal determination no less than that of billiard balls or ocean currents. For example, a man pauses at a junction, undecided along which of two routes to proceed. The route that he eventually takes is the inevitable one, being the resultant of a balancing out of conflicting action tendencies. Each of these owes its strength partly to physiological conditions and partly to the incipient reactions evoked by the particular assortment of stimuli (internal and external) making impact upon him at the time of decision.

The general attitude of the behavior therapist to his patients is in accord with this deterministic outlook. He regards the patient as a joint product of his physical endowment and of the molding influence of the succession of environments through which he—an organism—has passed. Each environment, each exposure to stimulation, has modified, through learning, the character of the organism to a greater or lesser extent.

Since the patient has had no choice in becoming what he is, it is incongruous to blame him for having gone awry, or to disparage him for maintaining his unhappy state. The behavior therapist therefore does not moralize to his patient, but on the contrary goes out of his way to nullify the self-blame that social conditioning may have engendered and that may have been magnified by the statements of friends and, perhaps, by previous therapists. The behavior therapist schools the patient to realize that his unpleasant reactions are due to emotional habits that he cannot help; that they have nothing to do with moral fibre or an unwillingness to get well; that similar reactions are easily induced in animals, who remain neurotic for just as long as the experimenter chooses; and that when the time comes when the experimenter decides to "cure" the neurosis, he applies to the problem methods that are determined by principles of learning. Just as the unlearning of the experimental neurosis is completely in the control of the experimenter, so the overcoming of a human neurosis is within the control of the therapist through techniques quite similar to those used in the laboratory.[1]

The patient thus orientated is now introduced to the practices of behavior therapy. This is done either by means of short didactic speeches, or else in the course of running discussions between patient and therapist that may include other topics.

The central role of fear (anxiety) in the neurosis must be brought to the fore at an early stage. Most patients are quite aware of being hamstrung by fear, but not so many recognize it to be the essence of their disturbed reactions. However, it is easy enough for most of them to accept it when the therapist points it out. The distinctive features of the origins of *neurotic* fears are brought out in statements on the following lines.

> You have realized that fear figures excessively in your life. It is necessary to have some perspective about this fear. It is an emotion that enters in a normal way into everybody's life whenever a situation involving a real threat arises, for example, walking alone at night in an unsavory neighborhood, learning that one's firm is about to retrench its staff, or being confronted with a poisonous snake. Nobody would come for treatment because of feeling fear in such situations. It is a different matter when fear is aroused by experiences that contain no real threat—such as seeing an ambulance, entering a crowded room, or riding in a car—to take common examples other than your own. To be fearful in such situations is obviously inappropriate, and can interfere with daily functioning in a most distressing way. It is this that we call neurotic fear; and it is the task of therapy to detach it from the stimuli or situations that provoke it.
>
> Let us consider how neurotic fears originate. The process is really what common sense would lead you to expect. Let me illustrate it by the old-fashioned example of the burnt child. The child places his hand on the big, black, hot coal stove. He quickly withdraws the painful

[1] It is notoriously difficult for recruits to behavior therapy who have previously been trained in psychoanalytically-derived disciplines to align themselves with this orientation. Even those who have become intellectually disenchanted with "dynamic" theories and practices lapse through habit into teleological modes of thought, and tend to make interpretive statements that often carry subtly condemning overtones. At best they tend to be noncommittal and unsupporting.

hand, tearful and fearful. His mother comforts him, but later notes that he keeps away from the stove and seems afraid of it. Clearly, the child has developed a beneficial habit of fearing and avoiding an actually harmful object.

But in some cases the experience also has another and less favorable consequence. Suppose in the mother's bedroom there is a large black chest of drawers. The child may have become afraid of this too—purely on the basis of its *physical resemblance* to the stove—a phenomenon known in psychology as generalization. Fear of the chest of drawers is neurotic because there can be no harm in touching it. It can have several undesirable implications. In the first place, the very presence of an unpleasant emotion like fear is objectionable where it is not appropriate. Secondly, the child is now forced to make a detour if the chest of drawers is in his path; and thirdly, he no longer has easy access to any delectable contents of the drawers, such as candy. In these features of this child's case, we have the model of all neurotic fear reactions.

Your own fears were likewise acquired in the course of unpleasant experiences, some of which we touched upon in your history. The unpleasant emotions you then had became conditioned, or connected, to aspects of the situation that made an imprint on you at the time. This means that subsequent similar experiences led to the arousal of these same unpleasant feelings. Now, just because these reactions came to be producible by particular stimulus triggers as a result of the operation of a process of learning, it is possible to eliminate them by the application of the principles of learning.

In animals the treatment of a neurosis is a very straightforward matter, especially when the experimenter himself has induced the neurosis. In human subjects it can be just as simple, but may be complicated by various factors in the more complex organism. However, endowed with language we can unravel most webs and our very complexity gives to human behavior therapy the possibility of a large repertoire of techniques.

Other kinds of orientating information are quite often needed. Although the patient can usually distinguish quite easily between those of his anxiety reactions that are adaptive and those that are not, there can be misapprehensions and many exceptions, and when they appear the therapist must spare no effort to remove them. It is not possible to decondition anxiety from a situation that the patient believes, however wrongly, to embody real danger. No amount of desensitizing effort can make a person indifferent to handling a snake he *believes* to be poisonous. Misapprehensions are particularly common in fears of the "hypochondriacal" kind. Only when the patient with recurrent pains in his chest is both assured that the pains do not signify heart disease and also shown their *actual* source can desensitizing operations be hopefully undertaken.

Some other kinds of corrective statements that commonly need to be made are typified by the following:

1. *You are not mentally ill and there is no chance of your going insane.* The bizarreness of their symptoms causes many patients to feel they are "cracking up", and their impression is strengthened when other people, and particularly doctors, do not understand what they are talking about when they try to describe their symptoms. It is often sufficient to express reassurance in an authoritatively dogmatic way; but with sophisticated patients a good deal of argument may have to be provided for the non-continuity of neuroses and psychoses. It must be explained that however bad a neurosis becomes it is still not a psychosis; that psychoses show a clear inherited pattern not manifest in neurosis; that there is evidence of biochemical abnormality in the serum of some psychotics, while neurotics are indistinguishable from normals; and that in the course of World War II, while the incidence of neurosis gradually rose that of psychosis remained stationary.

2. *All your reactions are explicable.* Patients who from time to time are overtaken by panic states or depressions, the antecedents of which are not clear, may come to feel chronically apprehensive; they do not know when the hidden forces will strike. Careful examination of the circumstances of these severe reactions almost invariably reveals constancies; and knowing them gives great comfort to the patient—in itself removing a significant source of anxiety.

3. *There is no virtue in confronting your fears.* Many patients, either on the basis of moralistic training, or urged by friends or therapists, feel that they should benefit by "facing up" to the situations that evoke anxiety in them. It is usually sufficient to refer to their own experience to convince them that this is futile and even aggravating. It is penance unrewarded by blessings.

They may be told how, by contrast, graduated and controlled exposures to disturbing stimuli may be therapeutically valuable.

Moral Issues

The *raison d'être* of psychotherapy is the presumption that it can overcome certain kinds of human suffering. Neurotic symptoms and related disabilities are the commonest source of suffering for which patients seek psychiatric help. The neurotic patient calls upon the therapist to remove his distress no less than if it were due to an organic illness, and it becomes the central task of the therapist to remove this distress. It is small comfort to tell a patient whose neurotic anxieties remain undiminished after treatment that he is cured because his personality has matured.

One result of realizing that neurotic behavior is learned is to place the responsibility for the patient's recovery unequivocally in the hands of the therapist, just as in other branches of therapeutic practice, and the patient should know this. If he does not improve despite earnestly cooperating in the programmes that have been set for him it must be for reasons that attach to the therapist. Perhaps there has been a faulty analysis of the case, or the techniques have been inappropriately applied, or none of the available techniques can offer a solution to the particular case.

In this last instance the therapist should frankly admit defeat, though he may offer continued "support" and also the hope that in time a solution may come to hand. We have had several cases with whom we have maintained contact after acknowledging "defeat", and to whom we have later offered opportunities of trying out new methods as they have emerged. More often than not we have ultimately succeeded—sometimes spectacularly. For example, in 1960, when one of us (J. W.) left Johannesburg, he handed over to A. A. L. a patient suffering from severe agoraphobia and fears of group situations that had been improving very slowly on systematic desensitization. For a time A. A. L.

continued in the same way, and then began to try out variations with no good effect, until he introduced the "shock-avoidance" modification of "anxiety-relief" conditioning (Chapter 8), which led to complete and lasting recovery in a matter of 3 weeks.

It must be evident from the foregoing that the behavior therapist must forswear blaming the patient when treatment does not succeed. He cannot attribute failure to "resistance", secondary gain, or other members of that family of popular alibis. He does not insistently "plug away" at one technique because he "knows" it is right and "must" cure, if only the patient will allow it to. Only evidence of change can justify a therapist in continuing with "more of the same".

Other moral issues concern patients. A good many of them question the morality of assertive behavior that is required of them for therapeutic purposes. They may be reassured in various ways. One useful approach has been to point out that there are three possible broad approaches to the conduct of interpersonal relations. The first possibility is to consider oneself only and ride roughshod over others, if necessary, to get what one wants. The psychopathic personality is the extreme expression of this basic attitude, and often, of course, falls foul of society. He has not been conditioned to feel guilty or otherwise anxious in situations in which most people are so conditioned. The second possible approach to interpersonal relations is always to put others before oneself. Such unselfishness is the extreme opposite of the psychopathic personality. The patient fluctuates between guilt at falling short of his standards of selfishness and the frustrations that result from self-abnegation. No less than that of the psychopath, though in a different way, this behavior has unhappy results. The Talmudic saying, "If I am not for myself, who will be for me?" recognizes the biological truth that welfare of the organism begins with its own integrity. The third approach is the golden mean, dramatically conveyed in this fuller quotation from the Talmud: "If I am not for myself, who will be for me? But if I am for myself alone, what am I?" The individual places himself first, but takes others into account. He conforms to the requirements of social living while acceding to the biological principle that the adaptations of the individual organism *primarily* serve the needs of the individual and not those of others. He fulfils his obligations to the group, but claims and is prepared to defend what he believes are his reasonable rights.

In the setting of this practical philosophy, it is usually a simple matter to decide what behavior is suitable to particular circumstances. While most of the resultant behavior would be acceptable to people of many backgrounds and many religious beliefs, there are instances that would arouse dissent. For example, if chronic unhappiness results from an unsatisfactory marriage, and all efforts to rectify the situation have failed, we do not hesitate to advise and aid the patient towards divorce, since we weigh the worth of a marriage solely in terms of human happiness. Marriage is not a sacred entity to be preserved for its own sake. Similarly, we do not shrink from attacking on rational grounds a patient's religious beliefs if they are a source of suffering. For example, finding that a patient was greatly distressed by the stern view taken by his church of some of his behavior, which included homosexual behavior, the foundations of the church's judgment were questioned and the patient was given a copy of Winwood Reade's splendid old book, *The Martyrdom of Man* (1872). Though he was upset by the criticisms of religion, the more rational outlook was not only a good thing in itself but facilitated psychotherapeutic procedures that eventually met with complete success.

In adopting the line of positive action the therapist assumes very grave responsibilities. It is therefore vital that he himself does not confuse the different aspects and has the craft to distinguish technical decisions from moral ones, and separate the tenets of his own moral code from the moral requirements of the patient's situation. London (1964) summarizes the issues as follows, in the course of an excellent and wide-ranging discussion:

> At the same level of abstraction, it is probably correct to declare that every aspect of psychotherapy presupposes some implicit moral doctrine, but it is not necessary to seek this level in order to say why it is important

> for therapists to recognize the moral concomitants of patients' problems and the implied moral position of some of their solutions. Some problems are inevitably moral ones from the perspective of either client or therapist, and some can be viewed as strategic or technical ones and treated without reference to particular value systems. In the one case, the therapist must fulfil a moral agency in order to function at all, whereas in the other he may restrict himself to the impartial helping or contractual function with which he is usually identified. But if he does not know the difference, then his own moral commitments may influence his technical functioning, so that he willy-nilly strives to mold men to his own image, or his technical acts may imply moral positions which he might himself abhor.

Our discussion of the moral aspects of psychotherapy cannot be concluded without reference to an objection to behavior therapy that is frequently brought up at lectures and seminars, though we do not recall seeing it in print. The complaint is that the behavior therapist assumes a kind of omnipotence in that his methods demand the patient's complete acquiescence, and this, it is felt, denudes the patient of human dignity. The truth is that the grade of acquiescence required is the same as in any other branch of medicine or education. Patients with pneumonia are ready to do what the medical man prescribes, because he is the expert. The same is the case when psychotherapy is the treatment required.

CHAPTER 3

The Gathering of Data and the Selection of Techniques

The Gathering of Data

Behavior therapy must always be based on an adequate behavioral analysis. The therapist needs to know the stimulus antecedents of all reactions of which the patient complains—his dreads, anxieties, panic attacks, depressions, compulsions, and others. The information comes from various sources—a detailed history of the origins of the patient's reactions, an account of the major influences on his personal development, certain questionnaires (detailed below), and the exploration of any areas that call for special attention.

The greater part of the initial interview is devoted to a chronicle of the patient's presenting problems. The therapist tries to extract as much detail as possible about precipitating events, giving the closest attention to the stimuli that were then acting on the patient—general and particular, exogenous and endogenous. The next step is to identify factors that aggravate or ameliorate current reactions. Aggravating factors are often the only available clues from which the therapist can detect a central anxiety source.

Considerable efforts are made to elucidate the social learning contingencies that have influenced and shaped the patient's behavior. The environments to explore are: (1) the *family environment* (interaction among and towards parents, grandparents, siblings, lodgers; modes of discipline and punishment, economic circumstances, and religious training); (2) *educational environments* (attitudes and experiences both academic and athletic at all educational levels; relationships with teachers, seniors, contemporaries and juniors); (3) *neighborhood life* (general tenor, interactions with peers, significant friendships and situations of threat); and (4) *occupational situations* (congeniality of employment, relationships with superiors and peers, handling of underlings). Experiences that seem to have been etiologically important are examined with meticulous care.

The history of the patient's sex life is traced from his first awareness of sexual feelings to his current mode of response. What were the circumstances and the age of the patient at the time of this first awareness? Did he masturbate and did this arouse fear or guilt? When did he start "dating"? The therapist needs to know what attracted the patient in each important "love relationship", and the course (and manner of dissolution, if any) of the relationship. If he is married or has a lasting liaison, details are required of the progress of the relationship in terms of social harmony as well as sexual adequacy. At every stage as much attention is given to interpersonal attraction, warmth and love as to physical sexuality.

A first essential in history-taking is to ensure clear communication. The meaning of every statement must be accurately determined (see illustrative interview, p. 30). The folly of taking for granted the use of popularly accepted terms is illustrated by the following experience of a 19-year-old girl admitted to hospital complaining of "depression". At a clinical meeting the psychiatrist in charge (not a behavior therapist) immediately began inquiring whether there was diurnal variation in her moods, whether other family members suffered from depression, whether she slept poorly and awoke very early feeling particularly depressed, whether she was inclined to indulge in self-reproach and whether she had lost weight. On the basis of her replies he made the diagnosis of "minor melancholia" and recommended a course of electroconvulsive therapy together with antidepressant medication. However, when a nursing attendant asked the patient to describe her feelings of "depression" she spoke of her general unhappiness and referred to "choking sensations", tachycardia, tremors and "restlessness". The psychiatrist then changed his diagnosis to "anxiety hysteria".

Anamnestic interviews may be considerably shortened with literate individuals by asking them to complete, at their leisure, a Life History Questionnaire of the kind provided in Appendix 1. Using the completed questionnaire as a guide, patient and therapist discuss each item and may quite rapidly obtain a comprehensive picture of the patient's past experiences and current status.

Information obtained from family members—friends, employers and associates—is sometimes useful for corroborating and extending material provided by the patient but, with rare exceptions, is sought only with the concurrence of the patient. This outside information is sometimes of assistance in defining the conditions that maintain and reinforce the patient's maladaptive responses.

In efforts to identify the stimulus situations that evoke neurotic responses, certain questionnaires have proved to be a great help. After experimenting with a number of these, we have found that two essentially simple and straightforward schedules elicit most useful and usable information.

(i) *The short Clark–Thurstone inventory*, which has come to be known as "Willoughby's Neuroticism Schedule" (Willoughby, 1934), when administered in a specific manner (i.e. with the therapist discussing the implications of each question with the patient before scoring) yields important information regarding present neurotic reactions in some commonly encountered (mainly social) stimulus situations, and also regarding general sympathetic reactivity (see Appendix 2). Much of this data does not as a rule emerge during the formal case history.

The total score obtained from the answers on the Willoughby Schedule usually reflects quite informatively on the severity of the patient's neurotic state. About 80 per cent of neurotic patients have scores of over 30 (Wolpe, 1958). But while high scores on the Willoughby Schedule denote high neurotic reactivity, low scores are no proof that neurotic reactivity is low. When therapy is successful in those areas where the questionnaire is relevant, a high score comes down proportionately. We have not known a score to decline when therapy has not been effective. However, our clinical observations need to be supplemented by controlled studies to determine the extent to which decrements in the score are due to possible regression effects and other contaminating variables.

(ii) *A fear survey schedule* (Wolpe and Lang, 1964) is a clinical instrument for surveying a wide range of disturbed reactions in a very short time (see Appendix 3). With the aid of this checklist it is often astonishing to find many areas of unadaptive anxiety that have eluded all other avenues of inquiry.

In certain cases, a variety of additional tests—both medical and psychological—may be indicated, particularly the Bernreuter Self-sufficiency Scale, and when it is desirable to determine a patient's standing in terms of extraversion–introversion the Maudsley Personality Inventory or its offshoot the Eysenck Personality Inventory.

Information-gathering is followed by *a delineation of the benefits* hoped for from therapy. The patient will naturally be hoping for the alleviation of the complaint that brought him to therapy. In addition, the therapist can very frequently promise other desirable results that successful treatment will afford *en passant*. For example, the patient with a stutter is likely to be treated by deconditioning of social anxiety; so that he may look forward to a removal of the discomfort *that may be present even when he does not have to speak*.

The Selection of Techniques

Even at an early stage the therapist may find it desirable to offer advice, reassurance, support, encouragement or clarification. If a patient is grossly inadequate in social situations, assertive training (see Chapter 4) may commence *immediately*. Having embarked on this, however, the therapist must not be deflected from exploring other sources of anxiety, guilt and depression. Most neurotic depression is the product of severe anxiety arousal.

In general it is expedient to give therapeutic priority to the patient's most pressing current problem. Thus, if a man who is acutely upset by his sexual inadequacies also has a fear of delivering speeches, the former complaint will receive attention first. (It is possible, of course, for these areas of anxiety to be interrelated.) The choice of strategy will depend on the degree of sexual inhibition, the stimulus antecedents of anxiety and the presence or absence of complicating features. In the majority of cases of sexual inadequacy the direct use of sexual responses as described in Chapter 6 is indicated, but where undue guilts and sensitivities complicate the issue, procedures like systematic desensitization (Chapter 5), assertive training (Chapter 4), the use of drugs (Chapter 7), and certain adjunctive methods like "anxiety-relief conditioning", thought-stopping, etc. (Chapter 8), may have to be employed. In cases that display particularly distressing and debilitating reactions, one tries to subdue these reactions as rapidly as possible. A compulsive vomiter needs to be prevented from vomiting before being treated for the fundamental areas of anxiety responsible for this distressing and embarrassing behavior. Similarly, it may be important for a school-phobic child to be coaxed back into the classroom before attempting to unravel and deal with family dynamics or particular conditions, even, sometimes, when these are responsible for the child's refusal to attend school.

Unlike the all-purpose brands of psychotherapy like Freudian analysis (in which all analysands are subjected to techniques of free association and dream interpretation regardless of the nature or sources of their problems), behavior therapy adapts to the exigencies of each individual case, determining the choice, order and combination of techniques to be employed.

Whatever the measures decided upon, it is of first importance to display empathy and establish a trustful relationship. The patient must feel fully accepted as a fellow human being, not less worthy, but perhaps less fortunate, than the therapist. It may be desirable to defer the use of specific counterconditioning procedures when there is reason to think that the patient needs to unburden himself or requires enlightenment or reassurance. At this point we take leave to chide some fellow behavioral scientists who, espousing notions of rigid behavioral engineering, imagine that one can do without such personal influencing processes. Considerable skill is required to tune the therapeutic relationship into the right key with diverse individuals. In acquiring this skill there is no satisfactory substitute for a personal apprenticeship followed by considerable clinical experience.

It is possible that certain personal characteristics assist individuals in becoming more effective therapists. Much has been written on this topic, but almost all of it is thoroughly speculative and without foundation in properly executed research. All that can be said at present is that the specific techniques outlined in this book need to be administered by persons who are able to treat their patients with respectful seriousness, and who can communicate a sincere desire to be of service.

Specimen First Interview

The interview reproduced here (with minor excisions) was selected because the *apparent* unifocal phobia led the therapist rapidly to uncover broad areas of the patient's history. The reader should attend to the manner and content of the questioning procedure. It should particularly be noted that the therapist goes out of his way to be permissive—condoning acts and attitudes that the patient seems to believe it natural to deplore; and that he tries to establish with great precision points that he thinks may be significant for therapeutic action. In this particular case one benefit expected from therapy was obvious—the removal of the phobia.

An inexperienced therapist might have been tempted at once to proceed with systematic desensitization, but the findings of the *second* interview (not given here verbatim) led in another direction, and incidentally illustrated with unusual clarity how unwise it is to plunge into the treatment of a case without an adequate understanding of it. Exploration of factors currently controlling the patient's phobia—a fear of knives—revealed that it became particularly strong when other people's children were unruly inside her house. Further questioning showed that she was extremely inhibited in almost all interpersonal situations, and habitually suppressed her anger because of a fear of disapproval. (Note that direct questioning failed to elicit the presence of suppressed anger during the first session (p. 32).) In keeping with all this, her Willoughby score was 66. The first therapeutic undertaking was, accordingly, *not desensitization but assertive training*. There could be little doubt that by developing an ability freely and appropriately to express her feelings she would remove a major emotional tributary of her phobia for sharp objects. As matters turned out, assertive training was rapidly effective, but though the phobia then became less troublesome, desensitization eventually had to be carried out.

THERAPIST: Dr. N. has written to me about you, but I want to approach your case as though I knew nothing about it at all. Of what are you complaining?

MRS. P.: I'm afraid of sharp objects, especially knives. It's been very bad in the past month.

THERAPIST: How long have you had this fear?

MRS. P.: It began 6 years ago when I was in hospital after my first child was born. Two days later my husband brought me some peaches and a sharp knife to cut them with. I began to have a fear that I might harm the baby with it.

THERAPIST: How long had the knife been with you when it occurred to you that it might harm the baby?

MRS. P.: I don't believe I let him leave it overnight, that night; or else we left it that night and then the next day—I think you could say—I told him to take it home. I can't remember exactly; I know I just didn't want it around. From that day to this I don't mind using knives as long as I'm with someone, but when I'm alone with the children I just don't want them around.

THERAPIST: Can you remember in what way the thought first came into your mind that you might hurt the baby?

MRS. P.: I can't remember.

THERAPIST: Now since that time, generally speaking, has this fear been the same all along, or has it got better or worse?

MRS. P.: Well, right after we moved about 5 months ago I felt a little bit better about it. At first, when I got home from the hospital, I made my husband take all the knives away from the house. I didn't want them around, so he took them to my mother's. I brought a couple back from her house when we moved. But I couldn't—after I brought them—I couldn't use them. I couldn't keep them out where I could see them and might pick one up and, you know—use it sometime.

THERAPIST: So what do you say in general—that the fear has been much the same?

MRS. P.: It seems the same. In fact, mostly I think that it's got worse.

THERAPIST: Is there anything—any situation—that you can associate with it getting worse?

MRS. P.: No. Only it just seems to be on my mind. Ah—if you don't mind me going back to something that Dr. N. said, he said that he thought now that it was more a habit—that I just didn't want them around. I mean I've just been thinking about that and—it's hard to admit—the children. I don't know why they make me nervous and I just am afraid that—that sometime it may get the better of me.

THERAPIST: Are the children making you more nervous—in the past month?

MRS. P.: Well, ah, you know in the summertime they stay outside and do their running outside; but in this kind of weather they can't get out, and, of course, they like to run and when they run in the house it does kind of get me.

THERAPIST: When you were in the hospital that time after your baby had been born, what was your general feeling about the situation?

MRS. P.: Well, I wasn't too happy in the first place because we had just built a house. I was working. I had just started to work and was working about 6 months when I got pregnant and I wasn't too happy about the whole thing then, because I liked my job and, building a house, we wanted new furniture and all that. Well, I suppose we neither one of us were happy about it. And I suppose that's the way it all started. And then just before the baby was born I said if it's a girl, a dark-headed girl with brown eyes, it will be fine but it turned out that it was blonde and a boy too. (*Laughs.*)

THERAPIST: Was that important?

MRS. P.: That it was a girl or a boy?

THERAPIST: Yes. Were you just joking?

MRS. P.: Well, no I don't think I was joking, because I really didn't much want it to look like my husband and his side of the family. (*Laughs.*) But he turned out to be the image of his Daddy. But I think that was a selfish . . .

THERAPIST: Well, that's all right.

MRS. P.: . . . on my part. It's probably a selfish way to look at it. I wanted a dark-headed girl.

THERAPIST: Well, you were expressing how you felt about the child at that time. It was just your feeling, and there's no question of right or wrong. It was your true feeling . . . Don't you like the way your husband's family look?

MRS. P. (*laughing*): I could never like their looks. I know they like me because of the way they act and . . . I wouldn't do anything against them.

THERAPIST: It is quite possible not to like the way some people *look*.

MRS. P.: I must have liked the way my husband looked or I wouldn't have married him.

THERAPIST: Then why was it important to you to have a child look like your family?

MRS. P.: Well, as I said, I think it was just selfish on my part.

THERAPIST: But, you had a preference. It is not a matter of being selfish. You had a preference.

MRS. P.: Well, I felt like I had to go through having and caring for the baby and all that, and I felt like I sort of wanted it to look like me since I had to go through it all.

THERAPIST: Sort of reward for your trouble?

MRS. P.: That's right.

THERAPIST: Did you ever have this sort of feeling before this child was born?

MRS. P.: Never.

THERAPIST: Well, I said that I wasn't thinking only about this feeling about knives. Has it ever happened before that you had a feeling of wanting to smash up things, maybe, if you were cross about them?

MRS. P.: I've always been sort of, you know, perfectionist. I suppose you'd say particular about my things. I had two younger sisters, and I know if they meddled with any of my things it . . . I would get awfully mad about that . . . but I never wanted to hurt anybody.

THERAPIST: Would you ever want to hit them?

MRS. P.: I don't think so.

THERAPIST: Would you ever want to hit anybody who annoyed you? Or when situations worked out the way you didn't like?

MRS. P.: I don't think so. I can't remember it . . .

THERAPIST: Well, it doesn't have to be a matter of hurting anybody physically, but just a feeling of anger and expressing anger towards people. Well, now let's get your background. Where were you born?

MRS. P.: Norfolk.

THERAPIST: How many brothers and sisters?

MRS. P.: Four sisters and one brother.

THERAPIST: And where do you come?

MRS. P.: I'm in the middle. There's two sisters and a brother older and two sisters younger.

THERAPIST: Will you just tell me how much older than you your eldest sister is?

MRS. P.: She was 47 in October . . . and I've got one who will be 45 in January, and my brother will be 43 in December, and then 18 months younger there's a sister, and one 2 years younger than her.

THERAPIST: Are your parents alive?

MRS. P.: Yes.

THERAPIST: What kind of person is your father, especially as you remember him in your childhood?

MRS. P.: Sweet and easy-going.

THERAPIST: Did you feel he was interested in you?

MRS. P.: You mean what I did at school and things like that?

THERAPIST: Was your father interested in you personally and in what you were doing?

Mrs. P.: Not very much.

Therapist: Did he ever punish you?

Mrs. P.: No.

Therapist: And what about your mother?

Mrs. P.: Well, I could say the same about her. They were both good—you know—provided. She . . . well she was interested, did things like driving us to school. She didn't seem to be too interested in how we got along or what we did, just that we got out of school. And I failed and I did very badly in school. She never talked to the teacher to find out if I could have done better, or anything like that. She never helped with homework or anything like that. Of course, I suppose she always had too much else to do. I remember when I was in high school there were all of us kids. There was the war and my brother was in the services and . . .

Therapist: Aside from the fact that your parents were rather similar people, would you say they sort of liked each other and also behaved towards you as though they liked you?

Mrs. P.: Well, they tried to see that we did right and I can remember they always took us to Sunday School and to church.

Therapist: Did they get on well together?

Mrs. P.: Well, yes. As far as I know. They had arguments.

Therapist: Did they have lots of arguments?

Mrs. P.: Well, no; after all, they lived together some 40 years.

Therapist: Were there any other adults who played an important part in your early home life—like grandmothers, aunts or nurses?

Mrs. P.: No, I don't remember any grandmothers or aunts.

Therapist: How did you get on with your brother and sisters?

Mrs. P.: Well, pretty good, I suppose. Of course, when you are children I think you fuss and fight lots of times. Now I think we all get along well.

Therapist: Did you have any particular fears when you were a child?

Mrs. P.: Well, no. Not that I know of. But when I was 8 years old our house burned down. I was on my way home from school and the fire engines passed us. It was in January and it was snowing like anything and somebody told us that our house was on fire. And that was a fear . . . it was. My parents lost almost everything they had. And I know they . . . oh, 5 or 6 years after that every time I would hear a fire engine I would get so nervous if I was in school I would have to get up and leave. I wouldn't leave the school, but I would have to get out of the class—but things like that don't bother me now.

Therapist: Did you have any other such experiences, or any other fears at all when you were a child?

Mrs. P.: No.

Therapist: Well, now, you said that you didn't get on very well at school. Apart from the fact that your studies were difficult, how did you like school?

Mrs. P.: I liked it fine. I mean I just played right along.

Therapist: Well, did you always do badly at your classes?

Mrs. P.: Yes.

Therapist: What about sports? How were you at them?

Mrs. P.: I might have taken after father in sports. I did well.

THERAPIST: Did you make friends at school?

MRS. P.: Yes, I had plenty of friends at school.

THERAPIST: Did you have any close friends?

MRS. P.: Well, yes. There were about six or eight of us that always chummed around together, girls and . . .

THERAPIST: Were there any people at school you were afraid of? I mean either among the girls or teachers?

MRS. P.: No.

THERAPIST: How far did you go in school?

MRS. P.: I finished high school.

THERAPIST: How old were you then?

MRS. P.: Eighteen.

THERAPIST: And then what did you do?

MRS. P.: I worked for a doctor for 3 years.

THERAPIST: As a receptionist?

MRS. P.: I did his labwork and typing, shorthand . . . helped with his patients.

THERAPIST: Did you like that work?

MRS. P.: Yes, very much.

THERAPIST: And then what did you do?

MRS. P.: I worked for a power company for 5 years, as a clerk-stenographer. I liked that too.

THERAPIST: And then?

MRS. P.: Got married. I didn't work for about 10 months. Then I worked for a plastic firm in Norfolk until the first child was born—as I told you.

THERAPIST: And since then?

MRS. P.: Housewife.

THERAPIST: How do you like being a housewife?

MRS. P.: Fine.

THERAPIST: Is there anything you don't like about it?

MRS. P.: That things don't stay clean when cleaned. (*Laughs.*) No, I like it fine. I wouldn't go back into outside work for anything. Unless I could work in a hospital, something like that. I should say something like that when my children are finished school.

THERAPIST: How old were you when you first had any kind of sexual feelings?

MRS. P.: Well, I . . . (*despairing gesture*).

THERAPIST: Well, roughly, were you 10, or 15 or 20? More or less.

MRS. P.: Well, I can't remember. I have no idea.

THERAPIST: Well then, was it before 10?

MRS. P.: I wouldn't think so.

THERAPIST: Was it before 15? . . . Before 20?

MRS. P.: Well, I would think it was before 20.

THERAPIST: Say about 17?

MRS. P.: Well, yes, maybe.

THERAPIST: In what kind of a situation did you have your first sexual feelings? Was it out with boys, or at the movies, or what?

MRS. P.: Well, I never had many dates. And when I was in school, well, in my class in school there just wasn't any boy. And . . .

THERAPIST: So, you started to have dates when you were 18 or so, after you left school?

MRS. P.: That's right.

THERAPIST: At that stage did you go out with lots of different boys or just one at a time? Did you go to parties? What was the pattern?

MRS. P.: Well, I went around with several. I belonged to the choir at church and whenever there were things like Sunday School parties we'd usually take somebody with us.

THERAPIST: Well . . . when did you first become especially interested in anybody?

MRS. P.: Well, let's see. I started going with my husband, Charles, I suppose in July of '49. And after I started going with him I never did go out with anybody else.

THERAPIST: There has been nobody else ever in whom you have been really interested?

MRS. P.: Well, when I was working at my second job, there was a boy there, but he was married, and I never did go out with him or anything like that.

THERAPIST: What did you like about him?

MRS. P.: Well, just everything. (*Laughs.*) And, ah, well, he showed me a lot of attention too. Then he left and went to Richmond to work and I never did see him again.

THERAPIST: So you didn't have any kind of going out with him or any physical contact?

MRS. P.: I know a lot of people wouldn't believe this but it's absolutely true.

THERAPIST: Well, then you began going out with Charles?

MRS. P.: No, I had already been going out with him previously, since the summer of '49, and I didn't stop work there until the summer of '51.

THERAPIST: What did you like about him?

MRS. P.: My husband is just . . . the way he . . . well, just everything I suppose. He was nice and the thing that impressed me with him most was the way he treated his mother. He was good to his mother. His father had been dead for a few years and he was good to her, and he always phoned her, and I felt that anybody who would be so good to his mother might be a good husband.

THERAPIST: Well, when did you feel that you were ready to marry him?

MRS. P.: I don't know if I ever did feel like I was. I went out with him for 7 years.

THERAPIST: Well, was he interested in marrying you earlier?

MRS. P.: Yes. Every time I would put it off. And I would say okay, and then I would get nervous and upset and couldn't sleep, and would say well I can't go through this again. So we would put it off again, until he got fed up with that. He was working, and when he got fed up he said he was going to quit his job and go to college. And he did.

THERAPIST: He went to college?

MRS. P.: Yes. From January '53 to June '56. And then he left to get a job somewhere else. When he left me sitting at home by myself I nearly died. I lost twenty pounds, I couldn't eat, I couldn't sleep.

THERAPIST: Well, can you tell me what the other man you mentioned had, that Charles didn't have? What points were important as far as your feelings were concerned?

MRS. P.: Oh, he was good looking. But I was thinking of my husband's blonde hair and blue eyes. He had dark hair and dark eyes.

THERAPIST: When you had the prospect of marriage to Charles before you and you felt nervous, what did you feel nervous about? Was there any particular aspect of the relationship that made you feel nervous?

MRS. P.: The whole thing, I suppose. I just wasn't ready to get married.

THERAPIST: In 1954 Charles went to study?

MRS. P.: January 1953. And he finished in '56.

THERAPIST: To do that he went out of town?

MRS. P.: Yes.

THERAPIST: So eventually you got married. When?

MRS. P.: In August of 1956.

THERAPIST: At that stage were you satisfied about being married?

MRS. P.: Well, he first of all phoned and said, "If you don't marry me now," he says, "we're finished. I'm leaving the country." So it was then or never, so I said "Okay". So we got married the next autumn.

THERAPIST: Well, how do you get along together?

MRS. P.: We get along fine. I knew I would never marry anybody else. Well, I suppose I'm just the type of person, you know, someone sort of has to say—Well, we are going to do it now or never.

THERAPIST: How is the sexual side of your marriage?

MRS. P.: Fine. I hope he'd say the same. (*Laughs.*)

THERAPIST: At this moment I'm only interested in your side. Do you have climaxes?

MRS. P.: Yes.

THERAPIST: Always?

MRS. P.: Well, no. I don't always, but I do at least part of the time.

THERAPIST: So you're quite happy in general about the marriage?

MRS. P.: Well, I wouldn't be any other way.

THERAPIST: What do you mean by that?

MRS. P.: Well, I mean I wouldn't be single again.

THERAPIST: But you have no complaints about the marriage?

MRS. P.: No.

THERAPIST: How many children have you now?

MRS. P.: I have two. The girl will be 3 on the 16th of this month.

THERAPIST: Do you like your children?

MRS. P.: Well, I should say I do.

THERAPIST: Except when they make a lot of noise and get on your nerves?

MRS. P.: Well, that's to be expected. I wonder sometimes what my mother did when there were six of us. Of course we weren't all there at the same time.

THERAPIST: Your children are quite well?

Mrs. P.: Yes.

Therapist: Do you like living in Richmond?

Mrs. P.: Better than I expected. I'd heard that the people were not too friendly, but I found out that they are.

Therapist: Is there anything you're not satisfied with?

Mrs. P.: Well, I would like to have a new house. We had to buy an old house and there wasn't anything to rent or to buy when we had to move, so we bought this old house and it still needs a lot done to it.

Therapist: What's your religion?

Mrs. P.: Methodist.

Therapist: Is religion important in your life?

Mrs. P.: Yes it is.

Therapist: Well, in what way?

Mrs. P.: Well, I don't think you can get along without it.

Therapist: Do you spend a lot of time with church activities?

Mrs. P.: Oh, no, no. I haven't been to church in Richmond. We have taken the children to Sunday School.

Therapist: Well, do you worry much about what God is thinking about what you're doing?

Mrs. P.: I do the best I can.

Therapist: Well, I've got enough of the important background information. I will give you one or two questionnaires to do as homework, and then next time you come here, we'll talk of the treatment procedures. We'll probably be doing a special kind of treatment called desensitization. It involves deep muscle relaxation and other special procedures. That is all for now.

CHAPTER 4

Assertive Training

THIS heading covers a range of methods of promoting change of behavior in the patient's life situation. Generally speaking, the patient to whom these apply has unadaptive anxiety-response habits in interpersonal relationships, and the evocation of anxiety inhibits the expression of appropriate feelings and the performance of adaptive acts. The therapist's interventions are aimed at augmenting every impulse towards eliciting these inhibited responses, with thc expectation that each time they are enacted there will be reciprocally an inhibiting of the anxiety, leading to some degree of weakening of the anxiety-response habit.

A basic assumption involved in the foregoing is that people have certain rights which they are fully entitled to exercise, and that proper human adjustment includes exercising them. While self-control and tactful restraint are necessary and desirable for civilized interaction, this can be taken too far. Those parents who, bound by convention and conformity, transmit stoic and ascetic habits of self-control to their children in the name of breeding, manners, good taste and refinement create what Salter (1949) has termed "inhibitory personalitiesjj.

Usually the interpersonal anxiety and correlated *functional inadequacy* are limited to the presence of particular categories of people or situations. Extreme cases live in an encapsulated environment in which there is very little freedom of expression. To outer view, such people range in profile from fawning sycophants who seek to ingratiate themselves with everyone to timid souls, obsessively and distressfully concerned about conforming to "proper" and "correct" behavior patterns. Some nonassertive persons are secretive, undemonstrative and aloof. They may confuse warmth with effusiveness and may regard all emotional expressions as being sickly sentimental or immature. They may hide behind asinine grins, vacuous handshakes, false compliments and other hypocritical modes of expression, sometimes allegedly because they are "good for business". There is in all a lack of integrity of *expression of basic feelings and emotions*. Whereas the normal individual can vary his behavior according to circumstances and suspend all assertive overtones in situations that so demand, the person plagued with interpersonal anxieties is unable to behave assertively even when most necessary.

When anxiety inhibits the behavior called for in interpersonal relations there are also undesirable *consequences*. The individual is almost inevitably left at an objective disadvantage *vis-à-vis* others, and often finds himself short-changed, if not empty-handed, in respect of his goals. His unexpressed impulses continue to reverberate within him, and as long as they do he is not at peace. In many cases these persistent discharges produce somatic symptoms and even pathological changes in predisposed organs, e.g. atopic dermatitis, asthma, migraine, peptic ulceration, of hypertension (see, for example, the case of Arthur B. (p. 45)).

Although the most common class of assertive responses invoked in therapeutic action is the expression of anger and resentment, the term "assertive behavior" is used quite broadly to cover all socially acceptable expressions of personal rights and feelings. A polite refusal to accede to an unreasonable request; a genuine expression of praise, endearment, appreciation, or respect; an exclamation of joy, irritation, adulation or disgust—may all be considered examples of assertive behavior.

Learning Mechanisms in Assertive Training

As stated at the commencement of this chapter, the central use of assertive responses is to overcome neurotic habits of anxiety responses in interpersonal contexts. The assertive behavior expresses and intensifies such counteranxiety responses as anger, with the result that any anxiety raised by the situation is inhibited. On the basis of this, inhibition of anxiety is built up. Meanwhile, the motor acts of assertion, if suitably applied, are usually followed by rewarding consequences of various kinds, notably diminution of anxiety drive and the attainment of dominance and control in social situations that were previously out of hand. The habit strength of these motor acts is consequently increased. *The counterconditioning of anxiety is thus intertwined on each occasion with the operant conditioning of the instrumental response*, and each facilitates the other.

Operant conditioning principles are employed alone when assertive behavior has to be shaped in those who lack it, not because of anxiety but because they have apparently never had the opportunity of acquiring the necessary habits. There are also some cases in which operant conditioning is used either alone or in combination with counterconditioning (Lazarus, Davison and Polefka, 1965).

The Gathering of Strategic Information

In clinical practice, patients usually reveal specific instances of interpersonal anxiety and associated inhibitions of action during their initial interviews—exploitation by friends or acquaintances; domination by a parent, spouse, or employer; undue deference towards authority figures, aged relatives, lifelong friends, and so forth. They may tell of indignities they have endured—behavior that, deliberately or inadvertently, has been unjust, offensive, degrading, inconsiderate, or vulgar and to which they have had no effective counter.

In deciding whether or not assertive training is indicated and if so, in what contexts, the therapist is guided by information obtained from the patient's life history, as well as from evidence of specific fears in interpersonal situations which may be derived from the Willoughby Schedule and other psychometric investigations. In addition, a questionnaire such as the following may be utilized, orally or in writing, *in toto* or in part:

Do you protest out loud when someone pushes in front of you in a queue?
Is it difficult for you to upbraid a subordinate?
Do you avoid complaining about the poor service in a restaurant or elsewhere?
Are you inclined to be overapologetic?
Would you be very reluctant to change a garment bought a few days previously which you discover to be faulty?
If a friend unjustifiably criticizes you do you express your resentment there and then?
Do you usually try to avoid "bossy" people?
If you arrived late at a meeting would you rather stand than go to a front seat which could only be secured with a fair degree of conspicuousness?
Are you able to contradict a domineering person?
If someone "stole" into your parking place would you merely drive on?
If a salesman has gone to considerable trouble to show you some merchandise which is not quite suitable do you have difficulty in saying "no"?
Do you generally express what you feel?
If you heard that one of your friends was spreading false rumors about you, would you hesitate to "have it out" with him?
Would you have difficulty in soliciting funds for a worthy cause?
Do you usually keep your opinions to yourself?
Do you find it difficult to begin a conversation with a stranger?
Are you able openly to express love and affection?
If food which is not to your satisfaction is served up at a restaurant would you complain about it to the waiter?
Are you careful to avoid hurting other people's feelings?
If you were at a lecture and the speaker made a statement that you considered erroneous, would you question it?
If an older and respected person made a statement with which you strongly disagreed, would you express your own point of view?
Do you usually keep quiet "for the sake of peace"?
If a friend makes what you consider to be an unreasonable request are you able to refuse?
If after leaving a shop you notice that you have been given short change, do you go back and point out the error?
If a policeman should forbid you to enter premises which you are in fact fully entitled to enter would you argue with him?
If a close and respected relative were annoying you, would you smother your feelings rather than express your annoyance?
Do you find it easier to show anger towards people of your own sex than to members of the opposite sex?
Is it difficult for you to compliment and praise others?
Do you have a close confidant with whom you can discuss virtually anything?
Do you admire people who justifiably strike back when they have been wronged?

This questionnaire is intended to reveal specific areas and degrees of assertive and nonassertive interaction. More information may be gleaned from discussing each question with the patient than from constructing a quantitative scale or insisting on "yes/no" answers. Though an individual may experience no assertive difficulties in relatively impersonal situations (e.g. complaining about faulty garments, poor service, short change, etc.) he may fail to assert himself in more intimate personal ones (e.g. contradicting a parent, saying "no" to a friend or criticizing a spouse). Some individuals may have little difficulty in voicing displeasure, but may nevertheless experience extreme disability in volunteering praise, or in expressing other friendly and affectionate feelings. Failure to assert is not a unitary trait; it is manifest wherever anxiety has been conditioned.

Assertive Training Techniques

Basic Strategy

To illustrate the use of assertive responses in implementing the reciprocal inhibition paradigm let us consider an individual whose domineering and aggressive mother frequently hurts and upsets him by hypercritical and vituperative outbursts. The son's natural resentment is seldom directly expressed because his previous training has foretold dire consequences from talking back to his elders or failing to honor his parents. He feels anxiety at any tendency to express his resentment and antagonism, and instead gives vent to pleading, sulking and withdrawing, or to protests that are either apologetic or petulant. It is not uncommon to find as time goes on that the "bottled up" anxiety intensifies and generalizes.

The patient is informed, usually with illustrative examples, like that given below, that the outward expression of his resentment will reciprocally inhibit anxiety, and that its expression on repeated occasions will lead to a cumulative conditioned inhibition of the anxiety responses. He is told how to apply the principle to various situations of his own. Giving instructions of this kind calls for discretion and good judgment on the part of the therapist, for the conquest of anxiety depends on the occurrence of overt acts of assertion; and the development of the assertive patterns is determined by the *consequences* of individual acts of assertion. If the son's expression of resentment provokes sharp, punitive retaliation, he will be more reluctant to make further sorties. The therapist needs a clear picture of the relationship if he is to minimize the likelihood of this.[1]

When difficulty is encountered easy assignments should precede major ones; or else, instead of advocating frank and outright expressions of resentment immediately, one may first show the patient how it is possible to gain mastery over certain interpersonal situations by subtle and covert forms of assertiveness (see Case 3). Gradually, the patient gains a feeling of control of a particular relationship and his self-assurance grows until a stage is reached when he can successfully carry through the direct expression of resentment wherever it may be necessary.

While in the initial stages of assertive training the requirement is to achieve the expression (no matter how clumsy) of previously inhibited affect, the mode of the behavior may subsequently be said to graduate from verbal bludgeons to the skilful use of metaphorical rapiers. Thus, whether upbraiding a subordinate, contradicting a colleague, or expressing a difference of opinion with a superior, there is a manner of doing so in which assertion is not mistaken for aggression. A way of distinguishing truly assertive behavior from inhibited reactions on the one hand and aggressive responses on the other is to ask oneself whether or not a given response would appear fitting in the eyes of an

[1] The son's changed behavior is also likely to alter materially the reinforcement contingencies operating on the mother and may thus modify *her* behavior. Generally, the patient's revolt constitutes a nonrewarding or even punitive contingency that leads to the substitution of more respectful behavior from her. But in some cases her attitude may harden and her hostility increase. It may then be necessary for the patient to have a course of desensitization beforehand (see Chapter 5) designed to render him impervious to his mother's outbursts.

objective onlooker. In practice this means noting one's own reaction to the thought of somebody else performing the response. By this device patients frequently obtain greater self-assurance in evaluating their behavior. It is sometimes difficult, of course, to draw clear lines of demarcation.

Assertive Training Procedures

Once it is decided that assertive training is indicated, therapeutic procedures usually commence with a description of ineffectual forms of behavior in general and their emotional repercussions. A reasonably articulate therapist can easily present a distasteful word picture of extreme inhibition with all its cringing and obsequious features. He points out that the sort of person who is unable to say "boo" to the proverbial goose and who treads warily through life, "letting sleeping dogs lie", appears socially unattractive. He may embroider the theme that poltroonish behavior is a negation of life and reduces potentially vital individuals to uninspired and uninspiring nonentities. Or he may focus on the enormity of the injustices that the patient meekly endures.

Such discourse as the above usually results in enough augmentation of resentment to quell the restraint of fear and permit the emergence of some assertive responses. But it may be necessary to apply additional measures to motivate certain individuals sufficiently. For patients with a strongly moralistic training logical arguments may be needed to convince them of the virtue of standing up for one's rights and the unavoidability (and justice) of hurting the feelings of those who flout those rights. For those who may draw comfort from the assurance that they do not fit into the category of "extreme inhibition" outlined above, the therapist should stress that all inhibitions of action that is desired and appropriate have negative sequelae. Reading Salter's *Conditioned Reflex Therapy* (1949, 1961) may be prescribed for its illuminating clinical material (but not for its theoretical position, which is at odds with a variety of facts) (Wolpe, 1954).

It is helpful to draw on past cases to illustrate to the patient what is required of him. A striking example is Arthur B., 38 years of age, whose fear of assertion was directly attributable to his father's deliberate schooling. The following adage was impressed upon him from an early age: "You are the master of the unspoken word, whereas the spoken word is the master of you." He was constantly told that the most urgent problems ranging from simple domestic crises to international upheavals would never occur if people spoke less. His father's favorite and oft-repeated joke was that "even a fish would not get into trouble if it kept its mouth shut!" Arthur B. has thus learned to "bottle up" his feelings almost entirely, although he was prone to occasional outbursts of rage. Not surprisingly, he suffered from gastric ulcers, asthma and tension headaches. On one occasion he felt himself close to suicide. The sequence of events which seemed to lead to this extreme feeling of despair was as follows. One morning his wife had made certain remarks which hurt and annoyed him. In his characteristic way, he said nothing, but left for work feeling somewhat upset. On arriving at work he was summoned into his employer's office and unfairly criticized for another employee's error. "I didn't want to squeal on him so I just kept quiet." Throughout that morning the employee in question kept laughing uproariously at the fact that Arthur B. had been so unjustly reprimanded. As usual, the patient made no overt response but felt inwardly angry and humiliated. Later that same morning one of the junior secretaries was extremely discourteous to Arthur B. Again he said nothing. He arrived home for lunch to discover that his brother-in-law had borrowed his tape recorder without his permission and had both snapped and entangled the tape. On this occasion Arthur B. reacted, but entirely out of proportion to the antecedent event. He directed an outburst of frustrated rage at his wife which only increased in intensity when she accused him of overreacting. Later, awareness of the fact that his anger was misdirected led to strong feelings of remorse. Added to this was guilt at the very violence of his response. All these emotions combined to give him a feeling of unworthiness and despair.

It is perhaps unusual for an individual to experience as many emotional upsets as Arthur B. was forced to endure on that morning, but the usual teaching of assertive behavior was applied. Arthur B. was told that he should not have left home that morning without at least informing his wife that her remarks were both hurtful and annoying and that he would discuss her attitude later. In dealing with his employer, he should have emphasized that he was not responsible for the error in question, without necessarily involving his colleague. If this was not possible and he had chosen not to denounce his fellow employee (though to do so would have been entirely adaptive and justifiable) he should have left his ungrateful colleague in no doubt about his anger at the mocking laughter. In short, it was impressed upon him that by dealing spontaneously with each such situation as it arises, the cumulative effects of tension may be entirely circumvented. Arthur B. required more than 4 months of assertive training before all his somatic symptoms disappeared. At a follow-up inquiry after 3½ years recovery had been fully maintained.

While being trained in assertive behavior, patients are told to keep careful notes of all their significant interpersonal encounters and to discuss them in detail with the therapist. It is necessary to know the circumstances of the encounter, the patient's feelings at the time, the manner in which he reacted, how he felt immediately after, and his own subsequent appraisal of the situation. The therapist, upon identifying disabling inhibitions, firmly stresses assertive as opposed to aggressive reactions where applicable. Play-acting, of prescribed behavior, known as *behavior rehearsal*, is often helpful. Where the patient's reaction pattern is considered deficient or inappropriate, he is required to re-enact the incident while the therapist plays the role of the other person(s). The therapist may then switch roles and act the part of the patient, sometimes presenting a deliberately overdramatized picture of assertion, thus affording the patient an opportunity for learning adaptive responses by imitation (cf. p. 134).

Some patients experience difficulty in identifying their own reasonable rights in given situations and are unable to determine whether or not an assertive stand may in fact constitute a usurpation of the other individual's rights. There are no facile formulae that one can offer in this regard, but the therapist should do all he can to clarify the issues. Numerous interpersonal incidents drawn from the patient's life experiences should be sought and the consequences and implications of assertive responses under those specific conditions should be fully discussed. In addition, it is helpful to cite data derived from other patients' case histories, as well as situations in which the therapist has exercised his own assertive prerogatives.

Most assertive trainees seem to follow a similar pattern of evolution. First, there is an increased awareness of their nonassertiveness and its negative repercussions. This is followed by an intellectual appreciation of assertive behavior and its positive effects. Increasing distaste for their own ineffectuality and resentment towards the forces which seem to be maintaining or reinforcing the nonassertiveness soon lead to tentative, usually clumsy, attempts at self-assertive responses. If positive effects ensue, the probability of engaging in more assertive behavior increases. Occasionally, as emotional satisfactions intensify and spread, previously timid and dominated individuals tend to overassert themselves. Negative environmental feedback combined with the monitoring of the therapist results in the necessary toning down of these responses. The patient learns to be dominant without being dominating. Assertion for the sake of assertion—a useful drill at an early stage—gives way to discriminative, adjustive responses. Finally, as the patient becomes aware of his growing mastery of interpersonal situations, there develops a genuine and fitting indifference to minor slights, petty machinations, small irrationalities and other insignificant "pin-pricks" of daily interaction.

It will be noted from the case illustrations below that an additional consequence of assertive training is a changed self-concept. More adequate behavior elicits positive feedback from other individuals, and this may modify existing negative self-perceptions in a way that facilitates the performance of the new behavior.

As a footnote to the forgoing we wish to suggest that when nonbehaviorally orientated therapists obtain favorable results this is often due to their patients having become more assertive. Although these therapists do not explicitly teach assertive behavior, the therapeutic interchanges may lead to a feeling of support which engenders such behavior. For example, in a series of cases reported by Seitz (1953) only those improved who felt themselves encouraged by the logic of the therapeutic situation to "act out", though the therapist discouraged it. A recent study by Storrow and Spanner (1962) seems to point in the same direction. Patients receiving "short-term, non-intensive psychotherapy . . . focused on attempts to help the patient understand the psychological causes of his illness" described themselves as significantly more *dominant* (i.e. "able to give orders", "manage others") after treatment. "Those patients who described themselves as more dominant after therapy than before, also tended to describe themselves as improved."

Case Illustrations

CASE 1

Mr. P. R., aged 38 years, complained of depression and described himself as an "occupational misfit". Although highly qualified in accountancy and economics, he held only junior positions in his work. He stated that he felt frustrated and demoralized. At the time that he sought behavior therapy, he had received promotion to the position of Assistant Chief Ledger Clerk in a large organization. This slight elevation in status, utterly absurd for a man with his excellent qualifications, tended to reactivate his personal misgivings about his station in life, and led him to behavior therapy "as a last resort".

During the initial interview it became clear that Mr. P. R. was grossly deficient in assertive behavior. The therapist lent him a copy of Salter's (1949) *Conditioned Reflex Therapy* and advised him to prepare a critique of selected chapters for his next session, a week later. The patient returned for his second session having carried out his initial assignment and stated that he felt hopeless about his future. "That chapter on inhibition made me feel that Salter had made a special study of me before writing it . . . I don't see how it is possible for a leopard to change its spots." The therapist provided a good deal of encouragement and reassurance but cautioned Mr. P. R. to make haste slowly. At the next session, the patient stated that promotion at work was a *sine qua non* for the acquisition of assertive habits. "I feel that until I am properly fixed up at work we will both be wasting our time." The therapist stressed that Mr. P. R.'s lack of assertiveness was responsible for his occupational failures, and that vocational advancement would have to follow rather than precede increased assertiveness. It was clear, however, that Mr. P. R. would use the work situation as the sole criterion for gauging his general improvement. A careful analysis showed that opportunities for advancement in his firm were extremely limited. It was obvious that Mr. P. R. would have to go elsewhere to achieve the desired elevation in occupational status, but he rationalized that he would feel less secure in an unfamiliar work milieu. Further enquiries revealed that Mr. P. R. abhorred the idea of being interviewed by prospective employers. This area was then made the focus of attention for assertive training by means of behavior rehearsal.

Mr. P. R. was told to pretend that the therapist was a prominent business executive who had advertised for an experienced accountant to take charge of one of his companies. Mr. P. R. had applied for the position and had been asked to present himself for an interview. The therapist instructed Mr. P. R. to leave the consulting room, to knock on the door and to enter when invited to do so (see below).

At the therapist's deliberately resonant "come in!" Mr. P. R. opened the door of the consulting room and hesitantly approached the desk. The therapist interrupted the role-playing procedure to mirror the patient's timid posture, shuffling gait, downcast eyes and overall tension. Mr. P. R. was required to sit at the desk and to play the role of the prominent business executive while the therapist re-enacted Mr. P. R.'s entry into the room. The patient was asked to criticize the therapist's performance. The therapist then modeled the entry of an "assertive individual", asking the patient to note the impact of variations in posture and gait and the all-important absence or presence of eye-contact.

The "correct" entry was rehearsed several times until Mr. P. R.'s approach to the prominent-executive-behind-the-desk was completely devoid of any overt signs of timidity or anxiety. He was then taught to deal with a variety of entries—being met at the door; the employer who makes himself incommunicado while studying important-looking documents; and the overeffusive one who self-consciously tries to place him at ease.

Next, the content of the interview was scrutinized. Mr. P. R.'s replies to questions concerning his background, qualifications and experience were tape-recorded. Mr. P. R. was instructed to place himself in the position of the prospective employer and asked to decide whether or not be would employ the applicant on the basis of his recorded interview.

It was clear from the recording that the elimination of Mr. P. R.'s hesitant gait and posture had not generalized to his faltering speech. Above all, it was noted that Mr. P. R. tended to undersell himself. Instead of stressing his excellent qualifications he mumbled rather incoherent and unimpressive generalities about his background and training. The therapist demonstrated more efficient verbal responses which the patient was required to imitate. In this manner, Mr. P. R. was able to rehearse adequate replies to specific questions, and to prepare an impressive-sounding discourse for use in unstructured interviews.

The above-mentioned procedures were employed during five therapeutic sessions held at weekly intervals. Mr. P. R. cancelled his sixth appointment and did not communicate for approximately 2 months. He then made another appointment. On entering the consulting room, he said, "You are looking at the Chief Accountant of . . . " (a very large industrial organization). He then described how he had replied to the advertisement, been exposed to three separate interviews ("You would have been proud of your handiwork . . . I handled them with such aplomb!") and how he was finally offered the post at an even higher salary than advertised.

Mr. P. R. proclaimed himself "cured". Although the therapist felt that many remaining facets of Mr. P. R.'s interpersonal dealings warranted additional assertive training, he did not discourage him from terminating therapy (on the understanding that he was free to resume should he ever deem it necessary).

Five years later Mr. P. R. telephoned the therapist to report that he had become principal economic advisor to an important mining concern.

Case 2

Mrs. M. S., aged 27 years, was referred for the treatment of a hyperventilation syndrome, panic, feelings of dissociation and frequent bouts of agitated depression. She had been married for 3 years and had twin sons 1½ years of age. The most relevant feature of her developmental history was the fact that she was an only child and had always feared her authoritarian father. Her problems had become manifest a few months after her marriage and had been intensified by a difficult pregnancy and labor.

Her condition improved markedly following a program of systematic desensitization to fears of death, and to various endogenous bodily sensations such as palpitations, dizziness and light-headedness (see Chapter 5). She nevertheless remained prone to bouts of depression and complained that she felt "personally unfulfilled".

It soon became obvious to the therapist that Mrs. M. S. was generally passive, overdiffident and excessively submissive. She evidenced considerable agitation when asked, "How much time do you spend doing what you really want to do, and how much of your time is spent doing things that other people expect you to do?" It transpired that Mrs.

M. S. enjoyed very little freedom in her day-to-day activities. Her husband was critical of her friends and was particularly envious of her close ties with one of them. Her parents expected nearly all her leisure time to be devoted to them and even insisted on choosing her clothes. Of special significance was the fact that her husband and parents agreed that she was too "nervous" to drive a car and also strongly opposed her suggestion that part-time employment would break the monotony of her existence. The patient wept and stated that she felt like a prisoner.

A "family conference" with Mrs. M. S., her husband and parents, during which the therapist endeavored to intervene on the patient's behalf, was rather eventful. The father insisted that he knew his daughter's limitations "better than anybody", while her timid and compliant mother only echoed the father's sentiments. The husband was less dogmatic, but it seemed to the therapist that he considered it financially expedient to agree with his father-in-law, who was in fact his employer. The father then demanded that therapy be terminated, whereupon Mrs. M. S. protested, "That's one thing you won't deny me! I'll pay for this out of my own money."

At the next session, Mrs. M. S. was extremely contrite and ambivalent about what her father had labeled "insolent, unwomanly behavior". The therapist emphatically lauded her for her "probably-first-ever-adequate-adult-response", and discussed age-appropriate and age-inappropriate behavior, stressing that in his estimation Mrs. M. S. was treated and behaved like a 7-year-old child. He emphasized that even a 7-year-old child could be expected to voice objections if others insisted on selecting her friends, her clothes, her leisure pursuits, and so forth. It was also emphasized that "femininity" and "assertiveness" are not at all incompatible. She was then advised to study Chapter 6 as well as selected case histories in Salter's *Conditioned Reflex Therapy* and to underline everything that she felt applied to her.

At the next interview Mrs. M. S. stated that she could see that her submissive and inhibited reactions were responsible for her recurrent bouts of depression and her attacks of panic. She insisted, however, that the feelings of guilt which had followed each of her assertive endeavors during that week were almost intolerable. She recounted how she had mildly reprimanded her husband for having played golf all day Sunday while she remained at home nursing her children who were ill. His retort was that he needed fresh air after being cooped up in an office all week, whereupon Mrs. M. S. immediately felt "mean and selfish". On another occasion when she expressed mild irritation at her mother's insistence that the children finish all their food, her father angrily shouted, "Your mother only means well!" Again the patient regretted having voiced her feelings.

The therapist discussed these incidents in detail, stressing that Mrs. M. S. was so accustomed to having her "private psychological territory rudely invaded" that she was unable to identify her own legitimate rights. It soon became evident that little headway would be made until she overcame her extreme hypersensitivity to criticism, especially from her husband and father. Systematic desensitization was accordingly administered along a "disapproval" dimension (the most relevant adjectives being "selfish", "inconsiderate", "mean", "ungrateful", "wicked", "stupid", "gullible", "nervous", and "cheap"). During the same sessions behavior rehearsal was employed to ensure that Mrs. M. S. would not be likely to find herself at a loss for words if and when these accusations were leveled at her. The therapist constantly goaded her to be more assertive at all times. It required more than twenty sessions before she was able to tolerate the idea of her husband or father directing these invectives at her, and before she was able to make adequate counter responses during behavior rehearsal.

The total duration of therapy was a little over 8 months. The formerly submissive, panic-stricken, agitated and depressed Mrs. M. S. now drives her own car, enjoys her morning job as a part-time secretary and has been free from anxiety and depression for over a year. She has persuaded her husband to launch a business of his own, a move which has proved a financial and personal boon.

Case 3

Although the most effective assertive response is a direct, frank and forthright expression of basic feelings, many situations exist where this is neither feasible nor advisable. Mr. G. F., aged 21 years, was an articled clerk in a firm of lawyers where he was receiving exceptionally good training and experience. The senior partner, however, appeared to take sadistic delight in finding fault with his work and would deliver unnecessarily lengthy lectures on petty details. Mr. G. F. observed that these harangues became the more prolonged whenever he endeavored to offer explanations in self-defence. The patient, an asthmatic, found that on nights following these "excruciating monologues" he invariably suffered from severe bronchial tensions. He had complained to the other partners without effect. He was reluctant to cede his articles and obtain employment elsewhere as he felt that this work situation embodied certain unique advantages.

Attempts to desensitize him to these verbal onslaughts were unsuccessful as there was an "all-or-none" quality to the patient's reactions. "Thinking about Mr. J. leaves me cold, but as soon as I picture that holier-than-thou expression and that condescending tone, my blood boils." The patient rejected the suggestion that an honest discussion with his employer at a time when he was not sermonizing might remedy matters. "That would be playing right into his hands", he insisted.

Therapeutic attention was then devoted to the implementation of subtle tactics which might serve to discourage the employer's prolonged and denigrating lectures. Mr. G. F. was instructed to make casual enquiries from the secretaries and other office personnel regarding the senior partner's idiosyncracies and possible vulnerabilities. At the next session the patient informed the therapist that the senior partner was reputed to be a hypochondriac. He added, "I don't know whether this is relevant but the typists are also very amused by Mr. J.'s great pride in his tailor-made suits."

The therapist asked Mr. G. F. whether he was able to feign a worried expression when his principal next engaged in one of his tirades and to interject with some assumed statement of concern regarding the state of his employer's health. He was exceedingly amused at the idea of this proposed gambit and said that he would certainly attempt to apply it. A second tactic was also proposed. In the midst of one of his employer's declamatory speeches Mr. G. F. was required to dust real or imaginary specks of dandruff from his employer's clothes. For this purpose behavior rehearsal procedures were employed in which the patient enacted this behavior with the therapist.

At the following interview, 3 weeks later, Mr. G. F. was jubilant. He described an occasion when his employer lit his pipe and settled back in his customary manner to deliver one of his harangues. Mr. G. F. recounted how he had riveted his gaze on his employer's left cheek and (approximately 10 min later) his employer had demanded to know what he was staring at. "I put on a worried frown as though my discovery was too dreadful to repeat and said 'Nothing, Sir. Excuse me for asking, Sir, but are you feeling quite well?' " The senior partner was reported to have replied, "Why, what's wrong?" whereupon Mr. G. F. said "Nothing, Sir, nothing at all." The interview was terminated less than 2 min later. Mr. G. F. subsequently used a variation on the ploys he had rehearsed. He had learned that his principal was extremely self-conscious about his balding head. "The next time he started with me I just kept staring at his head. The lecture ended after about 5 min instead of the usual hour or longer . . . I repeated the same performance 3 days later. Since then the boss has given me a very wide berth."

Mr. G. F. completed the remaining 18 months of his apprenticeship without further incident and was offered a junior partnership upon qualifying.

Tactics of the kind that Mr. G. F. found so successful are of a piece with the "one-upmanship" gambits made famous by Stephen Potter. We enthusiastically refer many of our more sophisticated patients to his books.

CHAPTER 5

Systematic Desensitization

Introduction

Systematic desensitization is the piecemeal breaking down of neurotic anxiety-response habits, employing a physiological state incompatible with anxiety to inhibit the anxiety response to a stimulus that evokes it weakly, repeating the exposure until the stimulus loses completely its anxiety-evoking ability. Then progressively "stronger" stimuli are introduced and similarly treated. This technique, which characteristically employs relaxation as the anxiety-inhibiting state, has made it possible for the first time to exert direct control over a great many neurotic habits. The therapist has been enabled to treat these habits in almost any order that he chooses, and as far as he chooses.

The employment of counteracting emotions to overcome an undesirable emotional habit *step by step* is evident in age-old methods of accustoming a child to situations that he fears by exposing him to small doses of what is feared in circumstances in which other emotions are also present. For example, if the child fears a visitor's black beard, he is quite likely to become reconciled to it by deconditioning events that may occur if he sits on his father's knee while the latter speaks to the visitor. He may at first essay intermittent glances at the beard upon which anxiety-arousal occurs against a background of warm and pleasant response to the father. The small fear-arousals are presumably inhibited and the fear subsides gradually, in concert with lengthening looks at the beard.

Besides being inadvertent agents to such spontaneous therapy, parents quite often "instinctively" treat established fears of their children in an essentially similar way (deliberately and fairly systematically). When a child is afraid of bathing in the sea, the parent will at first take him by the hand to the very fringe of the approaching waves and lift him up when a wave approaches. Then when the child has become comfortable about this he is encouraged to dip his foot into a wave, and later his ankle, and so on. Conquering his fear by degrees, the child eventually becomes able to play in the sea with pleasure. This is very much like the routines followed in primitive societies to prepare individuals to undergo ceremonial ordeals and in our own society in the training of mountaineers and trapeze artists.

The first known example of the deliberate clinical use of counteracting responses to overcome neurotic anxieties in piecemeal fashion involved the use of feeding to overcome children's phobias. It was reported by Jones (1924), who described her method as follows:

> During a period of craving for food, the child is placed in a high chair and given something to eat. The feared object is brought in, starting a negative response. It is then moved away gradually until it is at a sufficient distance not to interfere with the child's eating. The relative strength of the fear impulse and the hunger impulse may be gauged by the distance to which it is necessary to remove the feared object. While the child is eating, the object is slowly brought nearer to the table, then placed upon the table, and finally as the tolerance increases it is brought close enough to be touched. Since we could not interfere with the regular schedule of meals, we chose the time of the mid-morning lunch for the experiment. This usually assured some degree of interest in the food and corresponding success in our treatment.

The details of the use of this method are illustrated (Jones, 1924b) by the case of a boy Peter—"one of our most serious problem cases"—who recovered after treatment daily or twice daily for a period of 2 months. Jones was clearly aware of the role of hunger in the overcoming of the fear habit, noting that the effectiveness of the method increased as hunger was greater, and that "the repeated presentation of a feared object, with no auxiliary attempt to eliminate the fear, is more likely to produce a summation effect than an adaptation". It is this insight that gives her work an honored place in the history of the development of these techniques. It was an insight that was not shared years later by Herzberg (1941) or Terhune (1949), who also made use of graduated tasks in the therapy of neurotic patients, but proceeded empirically. (Herzberg, it may be noted, operated from a Freudian orientation, albeit a wavering one.)

In this chapter, after glancing at the factual foundations of systematic desensitization, we shall describe in considerable detail the usual procedures it comprises—relaxation training, hierarchy construction, and the presentation of imaginary scenes to the relaxed patient. We shall survey certain quantitative aspects of this technique, and then some difficulties and the means of overcoming them. Finally, after noting the existence of some variants of the technique, described in Chapter 8, we shall present statistically the results found in a small group of cases taken at random from the files of J. W.

The Formal Basis of Systematic Desensitization

Systematic desensitization technique has its formal roots in the experimental laboratory (Wolpe, 1948, 1952, 1958). In the neuroses produced in cats (see Chapter 1) by administering high voltage, low amperage shocks to them, while confined in a small cage, it was found that the anxiety responses conditioned to the cage and related stimuli and to an auditory stimulus that had preceded the shocks were extremely resistant to the normal process of extinction. Neither prolonged nor repeated exposure of the animals to the environment of the cage led to decrements in the intensity of these responses, even though the animals were never again shocked. The animals, however hungry, could not be tempted to eat attractive food scattered in the experimental cage. However, because they showed milder anxiety on the floor of the experimental laboratory and still less in a series of other rooms, graded according to their degree of resemblance to the laboratory, they were offered food in these various places in descending order of similarity. When, in a particular room, the evocation of anxiety was not great enough to inhibit feeding, successive offerings of food were eaten with increasing readiness while all signs of anxiety receded to vanishing point. The room next in resemblance to the experimental laboratory could then be dealt with. After a series of similar steps, eating behavior was eventually restored in the experimental cage itself, and this made possible the total elimination of all signs of anxiety even there. In parallel piecemeal fashion, anxiety was deconditioned from the auditory stimulus that had preceded the shocks.

While these observations led Wolpe to search for methods by which human neurotic habits might also be broken down bit by bit, they did not immediately suggest the systematic desensitization technique. This emerged only after a succession of further experiences in the course of a year or more. His first clinical endeavors were with techniques requiring direct behavioral changes in the patient's life situation, and the most successful of them was the instigation of assertive behavior. He was greatly encouraged in the use of these techniques on reading Salter's *Conditioned Reflex Therapy* (1949), and, in fact, was moved by its buoyant optimism to promote self-expressive behavior in all patients. But it was not evident how this could be expected to affect those neuroses directly in which the stimuli controlling the neurotic reactions were in no way brought into the interpersonal situations in which the assertive behavior was occurring.

And it soon became clear that, in fact, such neuroses were *not* responding to these measures. Conditioning theory requires that to eliminate or change a habit of reaction to a stimulus, that stimulus must be present in the deconditioning situation. Such deconditioning as occurs through acts of assertion can affect only the anxiety-response habits to stimuli that are present. If a patient has a fear of being alone, this will not be diminished by assertive behavior (if only because assertion implies the presence of another person), though certainly now and then benefit is noted in special cases in which a chain of other habits may be secondarily altered when interpersonal fear has been diminished.

Generally speaking, assertion towards persons is irrelevant where anxiety responses are to such nonpersonal stimulus constellations as enclosed space, animals, heights, the sight of blood—in short, all the classical stimuli to phobic reactions. It is also irrelevant when anxiety responses are to persons in situations where direct action on the part of the patient would be inappropriate; for example, where the fear is evoked by the mere presence of particular categories of persons, by being the centre of attention, or by a feeling of "rejection", such as may be felt when on a social occasion it seems to the patient that too little attention is being directed to him. A case in which the irrelevancy of interpersonal expressiveness was strikingly evident was that of a woman rendered severely anxious by all manifestations of illness in other people. Extremely comprehensive and effective schooling in expressive behavior brought about no change at all in her phobia, and the case was sorrowfully abandoned as a failure. At that time there was no discernible method of inhibiting anxieties aroused by stimuli to which no *action response* could be proposed for the patient.

Not long after this Wolpe had the good luck to come upon Edmund Jacobson's *Progressive Relaxation* (1938), which offered an anxiety-inhibiting response that did not call from the patient *any kind of motor activity towards the source of his anxiety*. He began to give training in relaxation to patients with phobia-like neuroses. However, it soon became evident that Jacobson gave his patients very prolonged and assiduous training (usually 50–200 sessions) because to inhibit the anxiety evoked by major real-life phobic stimuli a massive "relaxation potential" had to be learned. In a letter to J. G. Taylor, written in 1955, Wolpe described how the systematic desensitization technique emerged from efforts to diminish the investment in relaxation training:

> I began to organize programs of real life exposure to graduated phobic stimuli for patients who had acquired some facility in relaxing, usually after 6–10 lessons. But these programs were often very awkward to execute and I therefore began to explore the possibility of making use of imaginary situations under hypnosis. I was gratified to find that magnitudes of experienced anxiety diminished progressively at repeated

presentations of imaginary situations that were weakly anxiety-arousing, that increasingly strong imaginary stimuli could be divested in turn of their anxiety-evoking potential, *and that there was transfer of the deconditioning of anxiety to real situations.* At first, influenced by certain of Pavlov's experiments, I presented only one stimulus of a kind at a session, but cautious trials of multiple presentations produced no disadvantages and greatly enhanced the possibilities of speeding therapy.

General Statement of Desensitization Paradigm

The autonomic effects that accompany deep relaxation are diametrically opposed to those characteristic of anxiety. Jacobson (1939, 1940) demonstrated that pulse rate and blood pressure were diminished by deep muscle relaxation. It was later shown (Drvota (1962), Clark (1963), Wolpe (1964)) that skin resistance decreases and respiration becomes slower and more regular during relaxation.

Just as in the neuroses of cats where feeding successfully counteracts an anxiety response only if the latter is weak enough, so, in human subjects, the autonomic effects of relaxation are able to counteract only relatively weak anxiety responses. We have found again and again that a stimulus that evokes a *strong* anxiety response may be presented as many as twenty times to the relaxed patient without the strength of anxiety diminishing in the least. By contrast, if the anxiety response is weak, with successive presentations of the stimulus the amount of subjective anxiety becomes less and less until at last there is none whatever. Clinically, there appears to be an inverse relationship between the magnitude of anxiety a stimulus evokes and the ease with which its anxiety-evoking potential can be overcome by a given degree of relaxation. Quantitative psychophysiological research is needed on this point.

Once a weak stimulus has ceased to arouse any anxiety it is possible to present a somewhat stronger stimulus to the fully relaxed patient and this stronger stimulus will now evoke less anxiety than it would have done before. Successive presentations will bring the amount of anxiety aroused down to zero. Stronger and stronger stimuli are thus brought within the anxiety-inhibiting capacity of the subject's relaxation. To put the matter in another way, if there are ten stimuli which in their variations along a single dimension evoke degrees of anxiety in a subject which vary from one to ten, and if through the inhibiting effects of relaxation the anxiety aroused by the stimulus which generates one unit is reduced to zero, the stimulus originally evoking two units of anxiety will then be found to arouse only one unit. This is illustrated in Fig. 1. Thus, in an acrophobic subject who has one unit of anxiety produced by looking out of a second floor window, and two units by looking out of a third floor window, reduction of the amount of anxiety from the second floor window to zero would diminish the amount of anxiety at a third floor window to one unit. (For a more accurate mathematical statement see p. 90.) It must be emphasized that these decrements of response are not transient but lasting. As in the animal experiments, they are indicative of decrease of strength of anxiety-response habits.

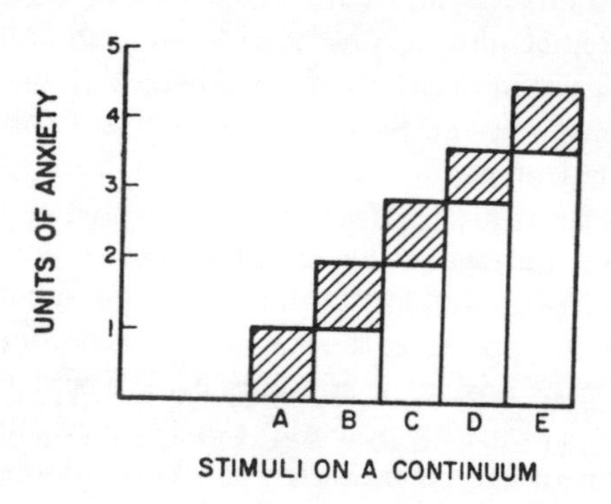

FIG. 1. Illustrating desensitization process. When *A*'s ability to evoke anxiety goes down from 1 unit to 0, *B*'s potential becomes 1 unit in place of an original potential of 2 units; and when *B*'s evocation is 0, *C*'s potential is 1 unit; and so forth.

The Technique of Systematic Desensitization

Before the therapist is ready to consider systematic desensitization, the problems posed by the case must be carefully considered, and if changed behavior is required, either in social or in sexual situations, this must be given attention. If systematic desensitization is indicated, it is conducted as soon as possible in parallel with whatever measures have been instituted in life situations. The technique involves three separate sets of operations:

1. Training in deep muscle relaxation.
2. The construction of anxiety hierarchies.
3. Counterposing relaxation and anxiety-evoking stimuli from the hierarchies.

1. *Training in Relaxation*

The method of relaxation taught is essentially that of Jacobson (1938), but the training is completed in the course of about six interviews, in marked contrast to Jacobson's practice. About 20 min of each of these interviews is devoted to it, and the patient is asked to practice at home for two 15-min periods a day.

In introducing the subject of relaxation, we tell the patient (who usually has already gained a general idea of the nature of conditioning therapy) that relaxation is one more of the methods in our armamentarium for combating anxiety. We continue as follows:

> Even the ordinary relaxing that occurs when one lies down often produces quite a noticeable calming effect. It has been found that there is a definite relationship between the extent of muscle relaxation and the production of emotional changes opposed to those of anxiety. I am going to teach you how to relax far beyond the usual point, and this will enable you to "switch on" at will the greatest possible emotional effects of an "anti-anxiety" kind.

There is no established sequence for training the various muscle groups in relaxation, but whatever sequence is adopted should be systematic. Our own practice is to start with the arms because they are convenient for purposes of demonstration and easy to check on. Next follows the head region because the most marked anxiety-inhibiting effects are usually obtained by relaxations there. (See also Appendix 4 for verbal instructions that deviate in details from the account given here.)

The patient is asked to grip the arm of his chair with one hand and to see whether he can distinguish any qualitative difference between the sensations produced in his forearm and those in his hand. He is told to take special note of the quality of the forearm sensation as being characteristic of muscle tension. He is also enjoined to observe the location of the tensions in the flexor and extensor areas. Next, the therapist grips the patient's wrist and asks him to bend his arm against resistance, thus making him aware of the tension in his biceps; and thereafter, by instructing him to straighten the arm against resistance, calls his attention to the extensor muscles of the arm.

The therapist goes on to say:

> I am now going to show you the essential activity that is involved in obtaining deep relaxation. I shall again ask you to resist my pull at your wrist so as to tighten your biceps. I want you to notice very carefully the sensations in that muscle. Then I shall ask you to let go gradually as I diminish the amount of force I exert against you. Notice as your forearm descends that there is decreasing sensation in the biceps muscle. Notice also that the letting go is an activity, but of a negative kind—it is an "uncontracting" of the muscle. In due course, your forearm will come to rest on the arm of the chair, and it may then seem to you as though relaxation is complete. But although the biceps will indeed be partly and perhaps largely relaxed, a certain number of fibers will still be contracted. I shall therefore say to you, "Go on letting go." Try to continue the activity that went on in the biceps while your forearm was coming down. It is the act of relaxing these additional fibers that will bring about the emotional effects we want. Let's try it out and see what happens.

When the patient has once again bent his elbow while the therapist pulls at his wrist, he is told to relax the biceps gradually. When the forearm is close to the arm of the chair the therapist releases the wrist, allowing the patient to complete the movement on his own. He then exhorts him to "go on letting go", to "keep trying to go further and further in the negative direction" and to "try to go beyond what seems to be the furthest point". When the patient appears to understand what is meant by these injunctions, he is requested to put both hands comfortably on his lap and try to relax all the muscles of both arms for a few minutes. He is asked to report any new sensations that he may feel. The usual ones are tingling, numbness, or warmth, mainly in the hands. After the alloted time the therapist palpates the muscles to assess how well they are relaxed. With practice he learns to judge gross degrees of muscle tension.

Most patients have rather limited success when they first attempt to relax, but they can be assured that it is a matter of practice, and whereas 20 min of endeavor may initially accomplish no more than partial relaxation of an arm, it will eventually be possible to relax the whole body in seconds. However, there are some fortunate individuals who from the beginning experience a deepening and extending relaxation radiating from the arms. This is often accompanied by more general effects, such as calmness, sleepiness or warmth.

We customarily begin the second lesson in relaxation by telling the patient that from the emotional point of view the most important muscles in the body are situated in and around the head, and that we shall therefore do these next. The muscles of the face come first and we start by noting the tensions produced by contracting the muscles of the forehead. These muscles lend themselves to a demonstration of the characteristic "step-like" character of increasing relaxation. The therapist simultaneously contracts the eyebrow-raising and the frowning groups of muscles in his own forehead very intensively, pointing out incidentally that an anxious expression has thus been produced. He then says, "I am going to relax these muscles in a controlled way to give you the feeling of the approximately step-like way in which decrements of tension occur during attempts at deep relaxation, but in actual relaxing the steps are usually much less rapid than in my demonstration." The muscles are then relaxed as stated, making an obvious step-down about every 5 sec, until, after about half a dozen steps, no further change is evident. Nevertheless, the patient is informed that relaxation is continuing and this relaxation "beneath the surface" is the part that matters for producing the emotional effects we want. The patient is then made to contract his own forehead muscles and is given about 10 min to relax them as far as possible. Patients frequently report spontaneously the occurrence of unusual sensations in their foreheads, such as numbness, tingling, or "a feeling of thickness, as though my skin were made of leather". These sensations are as a rule indicative of the attainment of a degree of relaxation beyond the normal level of muscle tone. At this lesson attention is later drawn also to the muscles in the region of the nose by getting the patient to wrinkle his nose, and to the muscles around the mouth by making him purse his lips and then smile. All these muscles are now relaxed.

At the third lesson the patient is asked to bite on his teeth, thus tensing his masseters and temporales. The position of the lips is an important indicator of relaxation of the muscles of mastication. When these are relaxed, the lips are parted by a few millimeters. The masseters cannot be relaxed if the mouth is kept resolutely closed. Of course, it does not follow that an open mouth is proof of relaxation.

At the same lesson, we usually include also the muscles of the tongue. These may be felt contracting in the floor of the mouth, when the patient presses the tip of his tongue firmly against the back of his bottom incisor teeth. Relaxing the tongue muscles may produce such local sensations as tingling or a feeling of enlargement of that organ.

Patients who have special tensions in the neck region are shown how to relax the pharyngeal muscles, which can be felt beforehand by the act of preparing to clear one's throat. Other muscle groups that receive attention only for special purposes are those of the eyeball (which are first individually contracted by having the eyes turned left, right, up and down, in turn), and the infrahyoid group (which the patient can feel by trying to open his jaws against resistance).

The fourth lesson deals with the neck and shoulders. Our

main target in the neck is the posterior muscles that normally maintain the head's erect posture. Most people become aware of them merely by attending to the sensations in the back of the neck. When they relax these muscles the head falls forward; but because the relaxation is incomplete in the unpractised individual, stress is imposed on the muscle fibers that are still contracted, and discomfort is frequently felt, or even pain. As Jacobson has pointed out, persistent practice while ignoring the discomfort leads to a progressive yielding of the muscles. The patient usually finds in a week or so that his neck is comfortable though his chin presses against his sternum. Those who find the discomfort of the forward-leaning head too great are instructed to practice relaxing the neck muscles with the back of the head resting against a high-backed chair.

Shoulder muscle tensions are demonstrated by the following routine. The deltoid is contracted by abducting the arm to the horizontal; the lateral neck muscles by continuing this movement up to the ear; the posthumeral and scapulo-spinal groups by moving the horizontal arm backward; and the pectorals by swinging it forward across the chest. In relaxing these muscles the patient is directed to observe their functional unity with those of the arm.

The fifth relaxation lesson deals with the muscles of the back, abdomen and thorax. The procedure in respect of the first two areas follows the usual pattern. The back muscles are contracted by backward arching of the spine, and the abdominal muscles as if in anticipation of a punch in the belly. After contracting them the patient lets them go as far as he can. The thoracic muscles (or, more accurately, the muscles of respiration) are necessarily in a different category—for total inhibition of breathing is not an accomplishment that we wish to promote! But the respiratory rhythm can often be used to augment relaxation. Attention to the musculature during a few fairly deep breathing movements soon reveals that while some effort is involved during inhalation, expiration is essentially a "letting-go". Some patients find it very helpful to co-ordinate relaxation of various other muscles with the automatic relaxation of the respiratory muscles that takes place with exhalation during *normal* breathing.

In making patients aware of the muscles to be relaxed in the leg it has been our custom to start with the feet and work upwards. The flexor digitorum brevis is felt by bending the toes within the shoe; the calf muscles by placing some weight on the toe; the peroneal and anterior tibial muscles by dorsiflexing the foot; the quadriceps femoris by straightening the knee; the hamstrings by trying to bend the knee against resistance; the adductors of the thigh by adduction against pressure on the medial aspect of the knee; and the abductors (which include some of the gluteal muscles) by abduction against pressure. All these muscles are the subject of the sixth lesson, and the patient should be allowed a good many minutes for relaxing them.

2. *The Construction of Anxiety Hierarchies*

This is the most difficult and taxing procedure in the desensitization technique. It requires accurate recognition of the stimulus sources of unadaptive anxiety response, painstaking itemization and careful grading of items. An *anxiety hierarchy* is a graded list of stimuli incorporating different degrees of a defined feature that evokes anxiety.

The defined feature common to the listed stimuli is known as the *theme* of the hierarchy. Some themes are easy to recognize in the physical stimulus situations that disturb the patient. In most classical phobias, the theme is plain to superficial inspection; fear of heights or a fear of dogs can be unequivocally related to the stimuli concerned. Other themes are quite difficult to discern, sometimes depending on a common internal response that disparate stimulus situations may evoke. The core of the disturbance is not immediately evident when a patient is upset at the news that an acquaintance has given a party the previous week. The disturbance may in fact be due to a feeling of rejection produced by the news, or perhaps to guilt because he feels he has failed in some obligation to that acquaintance.

To establish a rejection hierarchy or a guilt hierarchy (or others like them) requires detailed information about the patient's subjective reactions. Table 1 gives a sampling of hierarchy themes from thirty-nine patients (pp. 98–101).

Hierarchy construction usually begins at about the same time as relaxation training, and is subject to alterations or additions at any time. It is important to note that both the gathering of data and the subsequent organizing is done in an ordinary conversational way and *not under relaxation.*

The raw data from which the hierarchies are constructed come from four main sources: (a) the patient's history (Chapter 3); (b) responses to the Willoughby Questionnaire (Appendix 2), which reveals anxieties mainly in certain interpersonal contexts; (c) a Fear Survey Schedule (Wolpe and Lang, 1964), an extended version of which is given in Appendix 3; and (d) special probings into all possible situations in which the patient feels unadaptive anxiety. It frequently helps to set the patient the homework task of listing all disturbing situations that he can think of—events, thoughts or feelings that are fearful, embarrassing or in any way distressing.

When all identified sources of neurotic disturbance have been listed, the therapist classifies them into themes. Usually there is more than one theme. In most cases the themes are quite obvious, but sometimes one is misled. For example, a fear of going to movies, parties and other public situations may suggest a claustrophobia and yct rcally bc a fear of scrutiny. Frequently, fear and avoidance of social occasions turns out to be based on fear of criticism or of rejection; or the fear may be a function of the mere physical presence of people, varying with the number to whom the patient is exposed. One patient showed a fear of social situations that was really a conditioned anxiety response to the smell of food in public places. A good example of the importance of correct identification of relevant sources of anxiety is to be found in a previously reported case (Wolpe, 1958 p. 152) where a man's impotence turned out to be due to anxiety not related to any aspect of the sexual situation as such, but to the idea of trauma.

In the context of an attempt at defloration anxiety had been secondarily conditioned to the sexual act. In this instance the whole strategy of treatment was shifted by this realization from *in vivo* use of the sexual response to systematic desensitization of a traumatization hierarchy.

It is not necessary for the patient actually to have experienced each situation that is to be included in a hierarchy. The question before him is, "If you were today confronted by such and such a situation, *would you expect* to be anxious?" To answer this question he has to *imagine* the situation concerned, and it is generally almost as easy to imagine a postulated event as one that has at some time occurred. The temporal setting of an imagined stimulus configuration does not, as a rule, affect the responses to it. A man with a phobia for dogs has about as much anxiety to the idea of meeting a bulldog on the way home tomorrow as to the recollection of a previous encounter with this breed of dog.

Data from a patient whose anxieties generated much depression will illustrate some of the intricacies of hierarchy construction. The list is reproduced exactly as the patient first presented it.

Raw List of Fears

1. High altitudes.
2. Elevators (lifts).
3. Crowded places.
4. Church.
5. Darkness—movies, etc.
6. Being alone.
7. Marital relations (pregnancy).
8. Walking any distance.
9. Death.
10. Accidents.
11. Fire.
12. Fainting.
13. Falling back.
14. Injections.
15. Medications.
16. Fear of the unknown.
17. Losing my mind.
18. Locked doors.
19. Amusement park rides.
20. Steep stairways.

With the help of a little clarification from the patient the items were sorted into thematic groups as follows:

A. Acrophobia

1. High altitudes.
19. Amusement park rides.
20. Steep stairways.

B. Claustrophobia

2. Elevators.
3. Crowded places.
4. Church.
5. Movies (darkness factor).
18. Locked doors.

C. Agoraphobia
6. Being alone.
8. Walking any distance (alone).

D. Illness and its Associations
12. Fainting.
13. Falling back.
14. Injections.
15. Medications.

E. Basically Objective Fears
7. Marital relations (pregnancy).
9. Death.
10. Accidents.
11. Fire.
16. Fear of the unknown.
17. Losing my mind.

Before considering the hierarchical groups A–D to which desensitization is relevant some remarks must be made about group E. The patient's fears of pregnancy, accidents, death and fire were all reasonable, but her apprehension about these matters was more than normal, though not greatly so. It seemed that they might be a function of a generally elevated level of anxiety which would probably disappear when the major neurotic anxiety sources had been removed by therapy. Her fear of the unknown was bound up with the idea of death. Her fear of losing her mind, an inference from the bizarre and uncontrollable feelings that characterized her neurosis, was partly overcome by strong assurances from the therapist that her condition had nothing to do with insanity and could *never* lead to it, assurances that he reinforced by demonstrating that hyperventilation could precipitate many of her symptoms. There are some cases in whom *all* fears would belong in group E, in which case desensitization would not be relevant and thought-stopping would then probably be the most important technique to use.

On scrutinizing the stimulus groups A–D the reader will at once observe that the items are very general and not sufficiently well defined for hierarchical ranking. In fact, the items of each group are merely *categories* that will generate specific stimulus situations as the outcome of further communication between patient and therapist. Take, for example, group A—acrophobia. Each of the three items given refers to a whole range of concrete situations. They do not have the specificity that would permit them to be used in desensitization; but particularizing within the areas they encompass yields the concrete situations from which to construct properly calibrated hierarchies. In this case further questioning revealed that increasing heights evoked commensurate fear starting from about 20 feet (or a second floor window) and that at all heights motion aggravated the fear. Similarly, group D led to a fairly extensive hierarchy, of which some items, ranked in descending order, were:

1. Feeling of being about to lose consciousness.
2. Feeling of falling backwards.
3. Marked dizziness.
4. Feeling of lightness in the head.
5. Moderate dizziness.
6. Smell of ether.
7. Receiving an injection.
8. Racing heart (anxiety increasing with rapidity of heartbeat).
9. Weak knees.
10. Seeing syringe poised for an injection.
11. Sight of bandages.

It may be observed that the stronger stimuli 1–5 are all endogenous, and most of the weaker ones exogenous. What is common to all is the feeling of personal threat.

In other cases, besides multiplicity of hierarchies, one encounters multiple "dimensions" within a single hierarchy. For example, in a patient having claustrophic reactions in social situations, five variables controlled the intensity of the reactions. The reactions were the *stronger*:

1. The greater the number of people present.
2. The more strange the people.
3. The greater the difficulties in the way of leaving the room (both physical factors and social propriety being relevant).
4. The shorter the time since her last meal (this factor determining the measure of a fear of vomiting).

They were *weaker* if she was accompanied by:

5. Protective persons—husband, mother and close friend (in descending order of effectiveness).

Sometimes the most difficult problems of hierarchy construction become evident only after attempts at desensitization have begun and it is seen that the anxiety level does not diminish at repeated presentations of the weakest scenes contained in the hierarchies. The quality of the relaxation should be checked. If it is manifestly good the problem is to seek still *weaker* scenes, whose evoked anxiety can be inhibited by the relaxation. In many cases it is obvious where to look for weaker items. For example, in a patient who had an anxiety hierarchy on the theme of loneliness, the weakest item in the original hierarchy—being at home accompanied only by her daughter—provoked more anxiety than was manageable. To obtain a weaker starting point all that was needed was to add to her daughter two or more companions. But it is not always so easy, and the therapist may have to use a good deal of ingenuity to find manipulable dimensions.

For example, following an accident 3 years previously, a woman patient had developed severe anxiety reactions to the sight of approaching motor cars. The therapist had been led to believe that the patient noticed the first glimmerings of anxiety when a car was two blocks away, and that the anxiety gradually increased until the distance measured half a block, and then rose more steeply as the distance grew less. This seemed to promise straightforward progress, but at the first desensitization session, even at an imagined distance of two blocks, the oncoming car aroused anxiety too great to be inhibited by the counteraction of relaxation. Further investigation revealed that the patient had considerable anxiety at the very prospect of even the shortest journey by car, since the whole range of threatening possibilities was already present for her the moment a journey became imminent. But she had not thought this amount of anxiety worthy of report. As in all other cases, desensitization could not begin unless the amount of "danger" contained in scenes from the hierarchy was under control. A sharp delimitation of the implications of each situation was required. Accordingly, an imaginary enclosed field two blocks square was drawn on paper. The patient's car was "placed" in one corner of the field and the early items of the hierarchy came to consist of a trusted person "Dr. G." driving his car up to a stated point towards her car, and then to ever closer agreed points as the patient progressed. The "danger" was thus always circumscribed. Further steps consisted of drawing intersecting roads within the field, with a traffic light at which the patient's car stopped while Dr. G.'s car passed through on the green light. Later, progressively increasing numbers of strange cars were introduced. The transition to real situations was effected by "making" continuous with the public highway system the roadway on which these various cars were passing. (For a detailed account of this case see Wolpe, 1962.)

Another case where the procurement of sufficiently weak anxiety-evoking stimuli presented a problem involved a patient with a death phobia, whose items ranged in descending order from human corpses to funeral processions and dead dogs. Presentations of scenes of dead dogs produced marked and undiminishing anxiety, even when they were imagined at distances of two or three hundred yards (where they were hardly discernible). A solution was found in the use of a temporal dimension, beginning with the historically inaccurate sentence, "William the Conqueror was killed at the Battle of Hastings in 1066." (William seemed more "real" than the slain Saxon, Harold.)

An ever-present question in constructing hierarchies is whether the items constitute a reasonably spaced progression. If items are too similar, time will be wasted. If adjacent items differ too widely in anxiety-evoking potential, progress will be halted on moving from the lesser to the greater, and the patient may even sometimes be further sensitized, i.e. conditioned to higher levels of anxiety as the result of severe anxiety being evoked. When a hierarchy is based on a directly measurable dimension such as distance, a well spaced progression is relatively easy to obtain, though it would be a serious error to assume that it is a linear function. It has in fact been shown (Wolpe, 1963) that a simple power function is involved, whose exponent exceeds unity in some cases and is fractional in others. This subject matter is presented in more detail below (pp. 86) where it will be seen that the character of the curve is consistent for each type of phobia considered.

The problem of determining reasonably evenly spaced differences is much more difficult when the hierarchy does not depend upon an externally measurable independent dimension, i.e. when it depends upon secondary generalization such as being based on feelings of rejection. This, and many other difficulties of quantification that arise, not only in desensitization but in psychotherapy in general, are greatly aided by the use of a *subjective anxiety scale.* This is constructed by addressing the patient as follows: "Think of the worst anxiety you have ever experienced or can imagine experiencing, and assign to this the number 100. Now think of the state of being absolutely calm, and call this zero. Now you have a scale. On this scale how do you rate yourself at this moment?" Most patients can give a figure with little difficulty, and with practice become able to indicate their feelings with increasing confidence, in a way that is much more informative than the usual hazy verbal statements. The unit is called a *sud* (subjective unit of disturbance). It is possible to use the scale to ask the patient to rate the items of the hierarchy according to the amount of anxiety created by exposure to them. If the differences between items are similar, and, generally speaking, not more than 5–10 suds apart, the spacing can be regarded as satisfactory. On the other hand, if there were, for example, 40 suds for item number 8, and 10 suds for item number 9, there would be an obvious need for intervening items.

Some Examples of Hierarchies

1. *A Cluster of Hierarchies Involving People*

Case 4

Miss C. was a 24-year-old art student who came for treatment because marked anxiety at examinations had resulted in repeated failures. Investigation revealed additional phobic areas. The hierarchies are given below. All of them involve people, and none belong to the classical phobias. (Freedom from anxiety to the highest items of each of these hierarchies was achieved in seventeen desensitization sessions, with complete transfer to the corresponding situations in actuality. Four months later, she sat (and passed) her examinations without anxiety.)

Hierarchies

A. Examination series

1. On the way to the university on the day of an examination.
2. In the process of answering an examination paper.
3. Before the unopened doors of the examination room.
4. Awaiting the distribution of examination papers.
5. The examination paper lies face down before her.
6. The night before an examination.
7. On the day before an examination.
8. Two days before an examination.
9. Three days before an examination.
10. Four days before an examination.
11. Five days before an examination.
12. A week before an examination.
13. Two weeks before an examination.
14. A month before an examination.

B. Scrutiny series

1. Being watched working (especially drawing) by ten people.
2. Being watched working by six people.
3. Being watched working by three people.
4. Being watched working by one expert in the field. (Anxiety begins when the observer is 10 ft away and increases as he draws closer.)
5. Being watched working by a nonexpert. (Anxiety begins at a distance of 4 ft.)

C. Devaluation series

1. An argument she raises in a discussion is ignored by the group.
2. She is not recognized by a person she has briefly met three times.
3. Her mother says she is selfish because she is not helping in the house (studying instead).
4. She is not recognized by a person she has briefly met twice.
5. Her mother calls her lazy.
6. She is not recognized by a person she has briefly met once.

D. Discord between other people

1. Her mother shouts at a servant.
2. Her young sister whines to her mother.
3. Her sister engages in a dispute with her father.
4. Her mother shouts at her sister.
5. She sees two strangers quarrel.

2. *Some Variants of Hierarchies on the Theme of Sickness and Injury*

The examples that follow are given chiefly to illustrate individual differences in grading intensities of reactions. In all three cases there was fear of both external and internal stimuli, but in Case 5 the feared internal events had never actually happened. Cases 5 and 6 also had agoraphobia. All three required and received training in assertive behavior in addition to desensitization. In all cases the items are in *descending order of intensity of reaction.*

Case 5

Mrs. A. Z., married woman of 38.

External stimuli

1. Sight of a fit.
2. Jerky movement of another's arm.
3. Sight of someone fainting.
4. An acquaintance says, "That man across the street has some form of insanity."
5. The word "insanity".
6. The word "madness".
7. Insane-sounding laughter.
8. An acquaintance says, "That man across the street has an anxiety state."
9. The sound of screaming (the closer the more disturbing).
10. A man with a fracture lying in bed with ropes and pulleys attached to his leg.
11. A man propped up in bed short of breath because of heart disease.
12. An acquaintance says, "That man across the road is an epileptic."
13. Seeing a man propped up in bed short of breath because of pneumonia.
14. A man walks by with a plaster cast on his leg.
15. A man with Parkinson's disease.
16. A man with blood running down his face from a cut.
17. A person with a facial tic.

Endogenous stimuli

1. Having a fit.
2. Fainting.

3. Tremor of her hand.

Note: None of these possibilities had ever actually been experienced by the patient.

CASE 6

Mrs. B. Y., married woman of 32.

External stimuli

1. The sight of physical deformity in others, e.g. hunchback.
2. Someone in pain (the greater the evidence of pain the more disturbing).
3. The sight of bleeding.
4. The sight of somebody seriously ill (e.g. heart attack).
5. Motor accidents.
6. Nurses in uniform.
7. Wheelchairs.
8. Hospitals.
9. Ambulances.

Endogenous stimuli

1. Tense (explosive) sensation in head.
2. Clammy feet.
3. Perspiring hands.
4. Dry mouth and inability to swallow.
5. Dizziness.
6. Rapid breathing.
7. Racing heart.
8. Tense feeling in back of neck.
9. Weakness at knees.
10. Butterflies in stomach.

CASE 7

Mrs. C. W., married woman of 52.

External stimuli

1. Child with two wasted legs.
2. Man walking slowly—short of breath due to weak heart.
3. Blind man working lift.
4. Child with one wasted leg.
5. A hunchback.
6. A person groaning with pain.
7. A man with a club foot.
8. A one-armed man.
9. A one-legged man.

10. A person with a high temperature due to relatively non-dangerous disease like influenza.

Endogenous stimuli[1]

1. Extra systoles.
2. Shooting pains in chest and abdomen.
3. Pains in the left shoulder and back.
4. Pain on top of head.
5. Buzzing in ear.
6. Tremor of hands.
7. Numbness or pain in fingertips.
8. Shortness of breath after exertion.
9. Pain in left hand (old injury).

Desensitization Procedure

The stage is now set for the conventional desensitization procedure—the patient having attained a capacity to calm himself by relaxation, and the therapist having established appropriate hierarchies. It is natural to hope for a smooth therapeutic passage, and such is often vouchsafed; but there are many difficulties that may encumber the path. We shall first describe the technique and the characteristic course of uncomplicated desensitization.

The assessment of a patient's ability to relax depends partly on his reports of the degree of calmness brought about by relaxation and partly on impressions gained from observing him. By the second or third lesson, most patients report calmness, ease, tranquillity or sleepiness. A few patients experience little or no change of feeling. It would, of course, be a boon to be able to use objective indicators of degree of relaxation. Clark (1963) has employed the galvanic skin response, as have we also sometimes. Jacobson (1939, 1964) has used the electromyogram, but mainly as a corroborative measure. It is too laborious for routine use. But, fortunately, the reports of patients usually serve as a sufficiently reliable guide to their emotional state, especially with the help of the subjective anxiety scale (see above). Quite a number of patients, especially those who have little or no current

[1] This hierarchy was published in another connection in Wolpe (1958, p. 142).

anxiety, report a positive feeling of calm after only one or two sessions of relaxation training. In some fortunate individuals there appears to be a kind of relaxation–radiation zone (usually in the arms or face). These report a diffuse spread of relaxation to many regions with correlated growth of calmness when the radiation zone is relaxed. If the hierarchies are ready early it is our practice to start desensitization with those who can attain distinct emotional calm before concluding the relaxation training (though this is continued during subsequent interviews).

In embarking upon a desensitization program, it is, of course, highly desirable to achieve a positive feeling of calm, i.e. a negative of anxiety, but it is *not essential* and one is always well satisfied with zero subjective units of disturbance (suds). In a fair number of those who have considerable levels of current anxiety (whether or not this is pervasive or "free-floating" anxiety), it has been found that a substantial lowering of the level —e.g. down from 50 to 15 suds—may afford a sufficiently low anxiety baseline for successful desensitization. Apparently, an anxiety-inhibiting "dynamism" can inhibit small quanta of intercurrent anxiety even when it does not fully overcome a high level of current anxiety. But desensitizing effects are rarely obtainable with levels in excess of 25 suds; and in some individuals a zero level is a *sine qua non.*

When relaxation is inadequate, efforts may be made to enhance it by doses of meprobamate, chlorpromazine, or codeine given an hour before the interview. The choice of drug is determined by prior knowledge of what the patient responds to, or by trial and error. When pervasive ("free-floating") anxiety impedes relaxation, the use of carbon dioxide–oxygen mixtures by La Verne's single inhalation technique (see Chapter 7) is of the greatest value and with some patients comes to be used before every desensitization session. Inhalations are given until the patient reports no further decrements of anxiety, usually by the fourth inhalation. In a few patients who cannot relax but who are not positively anxious attempts at desensitization sometimes succeed, nonetheless, presumably because emotional responses to the therapist inhibit the anxiety aroused by the imagined stimuli. This is a supposition that requires experimental testing.

In about one-third of our cases desensitization is performed under hypnosis, which we most often induce by the hand levitation technique described by Wolberg (1948). The patient may have been hypnotized in an exploratory way on one or more occasions at earlier interviews, but quite often the first attempt at hypnosis is made at the first desensitization session. In those who are difficult to hypnotize and in those who for any reason object to it, hypnosis is abandoned, and they are told instead merely to close the eyes and relax according to instructions. We used to think that, in general, these patients made slower progress, but we are now very doubtful about this.

The first desensitization session may be introduced by saying, "Well, now, let's see how well you can relax and how you react to various stimuli and images. Don't worry. Our main aim at all times will be to keep you as comfortable as possible."

With the patient sitting or lying comfortably with his eyes closed, whether hypnotized or not, the therapist proceeds to bring about as deep as possible a state of relaxation by the use of such words as the following:

> Now, your whole body becomes progressively heavier, and all your muscles relax. Let go more and more completely. We shall give your muscles individual attention. Relax the muscles of your forehead. (*Pause 5–10 sec.*) Relax the muscles of the lower part of your face. (*Pause 5–10 sec.*) Relax the muscles of your jaws and those of your tongue. (*Pause.*) Relax the muscles of your eyeballs. The more you relax, the calmer you become. (*Pause.*) Relax the muscles of your neck. (*Pause.*) Let all the muscles of your shoulders relax. Just let yourself go. (*Pause.*) Now relax your arms. (*Pause.*) Relax all the muscles of your trunk. (*Pause.*) Relax the muscles of your lower limbs. Let your muscles go more and more. You feel so much at ease and so very comfortable.

At the first desensitization session, which is always partly exploratory, the therapist requires some feedback of what has been accomplished, and therefore says, "If you feel utterly calm —zero anxiety—do nothing; otherwise raise your left index finger." If the finger remains still, the next stage may begin; but if it is raised the therapist ascertains the level of anxiety by further probings—"Raise the finger if more than 10 suds", etc. This mode of inquiry is used, because it seems to cause much less disruption of relaxation than spoken replies.

If the patient continues to have a good deal of anxiety despite his best efforts at direct relaxation, various imaginal devices may be invoked. Those that we most commonly employ are the following:

1. "Imagine that on a calm summer's day you lie on your back on a soft lawn and watch the fleecy cumulus clouds move slowly overhead. Notice especially the brilliant edges of the clouds."
2. "Imagine an intense, bright spot of light about eighteen inches in front of you." (This image is due to Milton Erickson.)
3. "Imagine that near a river's bank you see a leaf moving erratically on the little waves."

If, despite these efforts, considerable anxiety persists, the session is now terminated. Otherwise it proceeds.

There is a routine manner of proceeding with the introduction of scenes at the first desensitization session, which is meant to yield pilot information. The observations that the therapist makes at this session frequently determine details of technique in compliance with particular requirements of the patient.

The first scene presented is neutral in the sense that the patient is not expected to have any anxious reaction to it. We most commonly use a street scene. Sometimes we feel it "safer" to have the patient imagine himself sitting in his living-room, or reading a newspaper; but there is no guarantee of safety unless the subject matter has actually been explored beforehand. At one time Wolpe used to employ a white flower against a black background as a standard control scene—until one patient evinced considerable anxiety to it because he associated it with funerals—and he had a death hierarchy.

There are two uses of a control scene. First, it provides information about the patient's general ability to visualize when aided by anxiety-free material. Second, it permits one to look for certain contaminating factors; the patient may have anxiety about relinquishing control of himself or anxiety about "the unknown". In either case, anxiety will be elicited that has nothing to do with the specific features of presented scenes.

The characteristic way in which scenes are introduced may be illustrated with reference to the case of Miss C. whose cluster of four hierarchies is given above (p. 74). When she seemed well relaxed she was addressed as follows:

> I am now going to ask you to imagine a number of scenes. You will imagine them clearly and they will generally interfere little, if at all, with your state of relaxation. If, however, at any time you feel disturbed or worried and want to attract my attention, you will be able to do so by raising your left index finger. First I want you to imagine that you are standing at a familiar street corner on a pleasant morning watching the traffic go by. You see cars, motorcycles, trucks, bicycles people and traffic lights; and you can hear the sounds associated with all these things. (*Pause of about 15 sec.*) Now stop imagining that scene and give all your attention once again to relaxing. If the scene you imagine disturbed you even in the slightest degree I want you to raise your left index finger *now*. (*Patient does not raise finger.*) Now imagine that you are at home studying in the evening. It is the 20th of May, exactly a month before your examination. (*Pause of 5 sec.*) Now stop imagining the scene. Go on relaxing. (*Pause of 10 sec.*) Now imagine the same scene again—a month before your examination. (*Pause of 5 sec.*) Stop imagining the scene and just think of your muscles. Let go, and enjoy your state of calm. (*Pause of 15 sec.*) Now again imagine that you are studying at home a month before your examination. (*Pause of 5 sec.*) Stop the scene, and now think of nothing but your own body. (*Pause of 5 sec.*) It you felt any disturbance whatsoever to the last scene raise your left index finger now. (*Patient raises finger.*) If the amount of disturbance decreased from the first presentation to the third do nothing, otherwise again raise your finger. (*Patient does not raise finger.*) Just keep on relaxing. (*Pause of 15 sec.*) Imagine that you are sitting on a bench at a bus stop and across the road are two strange men whose voices are raised in argument. (*Pause of 10 sec.*) Stop imagining the scene and just relax. (*Pause of 10 sec.*) Now again imagine the scene of these two men arguing across the road. (*Pause of 10 sec.*) Stop the scene and relax. Now I am going to count up to 5 and you will open your eyes, feeling very calm and refreshed.

She opened her eyes, looking, as is commonly the case, a little sleepy, and smiling placidly. In reply to questions, she reported that she felt very calm and that the scenes were quite clear. She stated that in both the scene belonging to the examination series and that belonging to the quarrel series there had been moderate anxiety at the first presentation, and less at subsequent presentations, but in neither instance had the decrease been down to zero.

It was noted that the responses of this patient were of the commonplace kind that do not presage any difficulties. Since visualization was clear, and there was evidence of decrease of anxiety with each repetition of a scene, it was predicted that we would make our way through all the hierarchies without much trouble; and the course of events bore out this prediction.

At this point it is worth remarking that even though the patient had a prearranged signal with which to indicate disturbance, the fact that she did not do so during a scene by no means proved that it had not disturbed her. Few patients make use of this signal when only mildly disturbed. But the provision of a signal must never be omitted, so that the patient can use it if he should happen to have a strong emotional reaction. *Exposure, and prolonged exposure in particular, to a very disturbing scene can seriously increase phobic sensitivity.*

All relevant facts about each desensitization session are noted on a card by a concise notation. The following record of Miss C.'s session given above exemplifies it:

> S. D. by rel. Scene 1—corner, 2—studying at home one month before exam. (×3), 3—two strange men argue across road (×2). Mod. decr. sl. 2, 3.

"S. D. by rel." stands for "systematic desensitization by relaxation". "Mod. decr. sl. 2, 3" means that the reactions to scenes 2 and 3 were initially moderate, decreasing to slight on repetition. Recently, we have been making increasing use of quantified subjective reactions (suds, p. 78) during desensitization; but the verbal type of statement is usually quite sufficient for practical purposes. The numbers in parentheses show how many presentations were given.

The usual plan followed in assigning numerical indices to scenes is to use an integer to indicate the class of subject matter, and letters for variations of detail. For example, in Miss C.'s case the imaginary situation of being at home working 2 weeks before the examination was given the index 2a, one week before the examination was 2b, and so forth. The advantages of employing these indices are: (1) they obviate repeatedly writing out the features of scenes; (2) they make it easy to find particular scenes when one consults the record; and (3) they facilitate later research work.

Procedure at later sessions takes much the same course as at the first, but there is a tendency for the preliminaries to take less and less time. When the patient is judged sufficiently relaxed, he is informed that scenes will be presented to his imagination and reminded that if anything should disturb him unduly he may signal by raising his forefinger. If at the previous session there was a scene where repeated presentations diminished anxiety, but not to zero, that scene is usually the first to be presented. But if at the previous session that scene ceased to arouse any anxiety, the next highest scene in the hierarchy will now be presented, except in the unusual patient who, though having no anxiety at all to the final scene at a session, again shows a small measure of anxiety to that scene at the subsequent one—a kind of "spontaneous recovery". This scene must again be presented until all anxiety is eliminated before ascending the scale. In patients who exhibit this feature, the need for back-pedalling can sometimes be eliminated by *overlearning* at the earlier session, i.e. presenting a scene two or three times more after it has ceased to arouse anxiety.

Quantitative Considerations

There is notable variation in *how many themes*, *how many scenes from each* and *how many presentations* are given at a session. Generally, up to four hierarchies are drawn upon in an individual session, and not many patients have more than four. Three or four presentations of a scene are usual, but ten or more may be needed. The total number of scenes presented is limited mainly by availability of time and by the endurance of the patient. On the whole, both of these quantities increase as therapy goes on, and eventually almost the whole interview may be devoted to desensitization, so that whereas at an early stage eight or ten presentations are given at a session, at an advanced stage the number may rise to thirty or even fifty. The usual duration of a desensitization session is 15–30 min; but Lazarus once conducted a session continuously for 90 min—until the fatigue of the patient compelled closure.

While the foregoing generalizations apply to the great majority of patients, there are occasional cases who, though experiencing no decrement of anxiety with the repetitions of a scene during a session, report decreasing anxiety to the same scene from one session to the next. The apparent reason for this is the occurrence of unusual perseveration of whatever anxiety was evoked by the first presentation. In patients who manifest this perseveration, only one scene should be given at each session. Perseveration of anxiety of varying severity may also be observed in the usual run of patients after the presentation of an unduly disturbing scene; and when this happens desensitizing operations should be terminated for that session.

The *duration* of a scene is usually of the order of 5 sec but it may be varied according to several circumstances. It is quickly terminated if the patient signals anxiety by spontaneously raising his finger or if he shows any sharp reaction. Whenever the therapist has a special reason to suspect that a scene may evoke a strong reaction he presents it cautiously and for no more than 1 or 2 sec. By and large, early presentations of scenes are briefer, later ones longer. A certain number of patients require 15 or more seconds to construct a clear image of a scene in their imagination. The character of the scene also necessarily plays a part in determining the time allowed for it. Striking a match needs less time than walking six blocks (Lazarus, 1964).

The *interval* between scenes also varies. It is usually between 10 and 20 sec, but if the patient has been more than slightly disturbed by the preceding scene, the interval may be extended to 1 min or more, during which time the patient may be given repeated suggestions to be calm, relaxed and tranquil. Until the therapist is well acquainted with the patient's modes of reacting, he should frequently check the basal relaxation level between scenes. Continuous GSR recordings would often fulfil this purpose admirably.

The *number* of desensitizing sessions required varies according to the number of phobias, the intensity of each, and the degree of generalization or involvement of related stimuli in the case of each phobia. One patient may recover in about half a dozen sessions; another may require a hundred or more. The patient with a death phobia, mentioned above, on whom a temporal dimension had to be used, also had two other phobias and required a total of about a hundred sessions. To remove the death phobia alone, a total of about 2000 scene presentations had to be used.

The *spacing* of sessions does not seem to matter greatly. As a rule, sessions are given two to three times a week, but may be separated by many weeks or take place daily. Some patients, visiting from afar, receive two sessions a day, and occasionally as many as four. At the opposite extreme, Lazarus overcame fears of criticism and of harmless snakes in a 43-year-old man in thirty-four sessions at monthly intervals, i.e. taking nearly 3 years. Whether sessions are massed or widely dispersed, there is practically always a close correlation between the extent to which desensitization to imaginary stimuli has been accomplished and the degree of diminution of anxiety responses to real stimuli in the phobic areas. Except when therapy is almost finished and nothing remains of a phobia but a few loose ends (that may be overcome through emotions arising spontaneously in the ordinary course of living) very little change occurs, as a rule, between sessions. In one case of severe claustrophobia a marked but incomplete degree of improvement achieved by a first series of sessions remained almost stationary during a 3½-year interval, after which further sessions led to complete elimination of the phobia. Similarly, a patient with a disabling fear of cars who had daily sessions for a week or two every 5 weeks or so improved greatly during the treatment phases and not at all during the intervening weeks (Wolpe, 1962).

Rate of change is neither haphazard nor purely an individual matter. At least in the desensitization of the classical phobias it follows consistent quantitative laws. A study of twenty phobias of thirteen patients (Wolpe, 1963)[1] was prompted by the casual observation that, during desensitization, the number of presentations of a scene required to bring the anxiety it causes down to zero is not uniform, but in some cases increases and in others decreases on the way up the hierarchy. An attempt was made to establish quantitative relations by a study of some classical phobias in which the hierarchy items lay on a physical dimension. The hierarchies concerned were grouped as follows:

1. Phobias in which anxiety increases with *decreasing* distance from a fearful object or situation (proximation phobias).
2. Phobias in which anxiety increases with *decreasing* space and/or freedom of movement (claustrophobias).
3. Phobias in which anxiety increases with *increasing* distance from a *safe* point or person (remoteness phobias).
4. Phobias in which anxiety increases with number of phobic objects.

It was found that in claustrophobias and proximation phobias desensitization needs relatively few scene presentations at first for a given measure of progress, and then more and more on the way up the hierarchy, so that the curve of cumulative scene presentations is a positively accelerating function. In remoteness phobias, and those where fear increases with numbers of feared objects, the number of scene presentations needed for a measure of progress is initially high and then progressively falls, the cumulative curve thus corresponding to a negatively accelerating function. No exceptions were found, as may be observed by studying Figs. 2–5, each of which contains the curves of a particular group. In order to make them comparable, the curves were subjected to percentile transformations. The horizontal axis shows attained percentage of criterion of recovery, and the

[1] Much of the material in this section is reproduced from this article.

vertical axis scene presentations as a percentage of the total number employed to overcome the whole hierarchy.

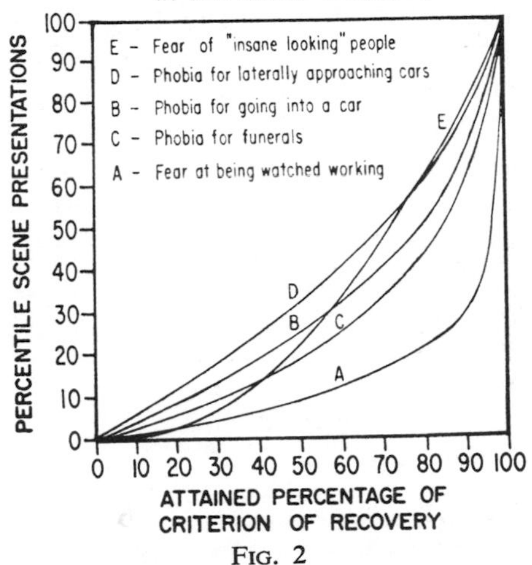

FIG. 2

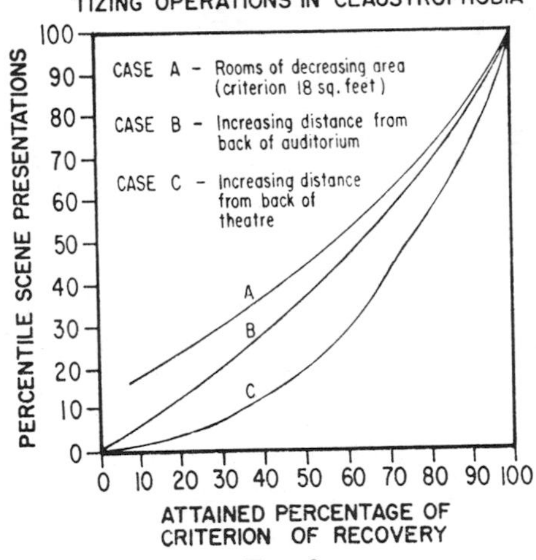

FIG. 3

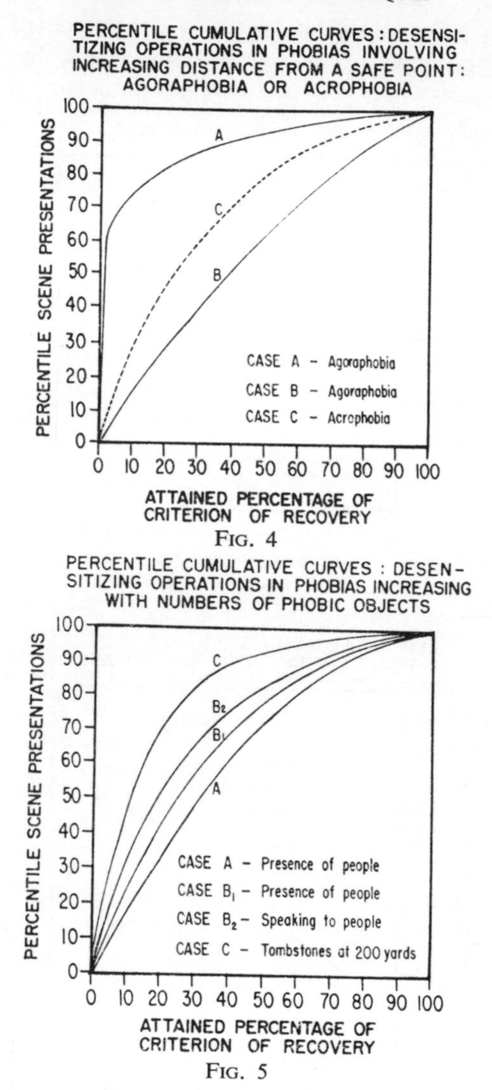

FIG. 4

FIG. 5

Figure 6 illustrates that it is not the personality of the patient, but the type of phobia, that determines the shape of the curve.

The three curves in this figure were obtained from a single patient. That displaying negative acceleration, *B*, delineates the desensitization of the anxiety response to an increasing number of tombstones at 200 yd. The positively accelerating curves belong respectively to proximation phobias to a dead dog, *A*, and to a stationary automobile, *C*, and are strikingly concordant.

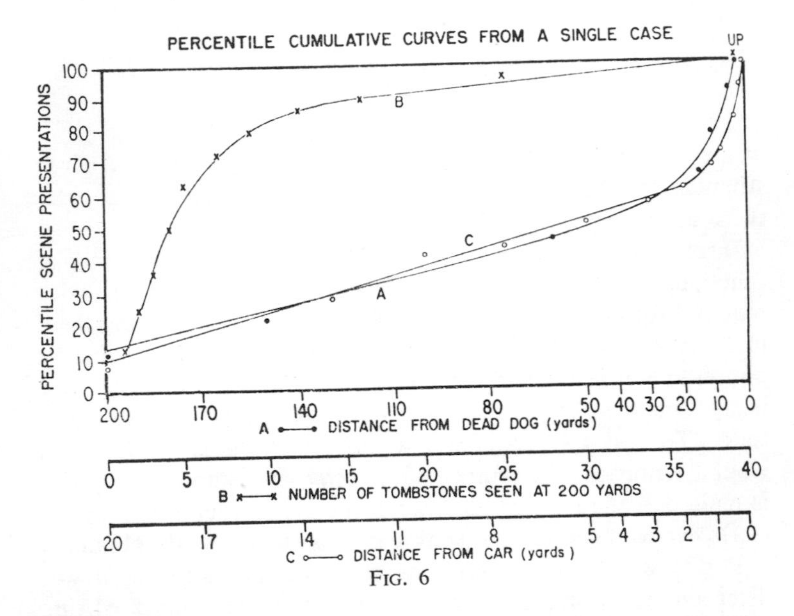

FIG. 6

Mathematical analysis of the curves reveals that with the exception of that for agoraphobia case A, and curve *C* in Fig. 5 (which will be commented upon subsequently), they express the same kind of functional relation as has been found by Stevens (1957, 1962) in relating the physical magnitude of a stimulus to its perceived intensity—the "psycho-physical law". This is a general empirical law that the psychological (subjective) magnitude is a power function of the stimulus magnitude. This means that to make one stimulus seem twice as strong as another, the physical energy must be increased at a fixed ratio, no matter what the initial intensity level. The relationship is expressed by the formula:

$$P=kS^n,$$

where P stands for perceived intensity (psychological magnitude), S for stimulus magnitude, k is a constant, and n the exponent of the relationship. The exponent is determined empirically by the formula:

$$n=\frac{\log 0{\cdot}5}{\log r},$$

where r is the ratio between the physical magnitude of a given stimulus and the physical magnitude of the stimulus that appears twice as strong as the given stimulus.

Insofar as the desensitization curves portray this kind of functional relation it may be deduced that the amount of work required for each measured unit of progress in overcoming these phobias is a function of the correlated magnitudes of the subject's pretreatment response, a relevant indicator of response here being *autonomic response magnitude* as well as perceived magnitude. To test this deduction an investigation is needed that would compare the curve of directly measured autonomic magnitudes of response at different points in hierarchies *before treatment* with the desensitization curves subsequently obtained.

For several of the curves the value of the exponent n was determined by Stevens's formula (see above), the value of r being derived from the point on the x axis at which $y=50$ per cent (0·5). Among the proximation phobias (Fig. 2) the exponent of the middle curve, C, is about 3·0. Among the phobias varying with numbers of phobic objects (Fig. 5) the value for curve B_2 is 0·43. The middle curve, C, in the remoteness phobia group (Fig. 4) is almost identical with this.

As mentioned above, curve A of the remoteness group does not conform to a power function, but the case was unusual in that the desensitization distances reflected in the curve ranged from 20 yards to 100 miles. It is obvious that a person's perception of difference of yards may vary in quite a dissimilar way from difference of miles. It was found upon plotting separate curves for 0–1 mile and for 1–100 miles that two power function curves were obtained, the first (0–1) being similar to the theoretical curve $n=0\cdot44$, and the second (1–100) conforming almost exactly to the theoretical curve, $n=0\cdot26$ (Wolpe, 1963). Curve *C* in Fig. 4 fits an exponential function $[P=76\cdot11\ (1-0\cdot85^n)]$ a good deal better than a power function, but remains close enough to the power curve $n=0\cdot3$ not to constitute a damaging exception to the rule.

Awareness of these quantitative relations makes it possible both to predict, in general, at what stages in cases of this class progress will be slowest, and, more specifically, to calculate, after treatment has proceeded long enough to provide the essential data, how much more treatment will be needed to overcome a particular phobia. Furthermore, the curves characterizing different dimensions help the therapist to decide which dimension to work with first in a multidimensional hierarchy. For example, in a woman with a dread of being seen vomiting the fear increased with numbers of witnesses and with proximity. Knowing that the numbers curve accelerates negatively and the proximation curve positively led one first to present increasing numbers at a distance—enabling the number dimension to be mastered with very little effort. If the reverse order had been adopted one would ultimately have had to contend with the steep sections of both curves simultaneously.

Some Snags and Pitfalls

Sometimes, despite having carried out the preliminaries conscientiously and apparently successfully, the therapist is chagrined to find that desensitization is not proceeding according to his expectations. Either the patient experiences no decrement of anxiety to successive presentations of scenes, or he reports no improvement in his reactions to real situations to correspond with progress during sessions. Human variations are so multiplex and so often subtle that even the most extensive experience can provide no absolute insurance against such disappointments. What matters most is to be able to retrieve the situation; and to do this the therapist must be able to account for his failure. The usual reasons are of three kinds, which will be discussed in turn.

1. Difficulties of relaxation.
2. Misleading or irrelevant hierarchies.
3. Inadequacies of imagery.

1. *Difficulties of Relaxation*

Sometimes the patient states that he is well relaxed when in fact he is not. This may happen either because he is not sufficiently aware of the internal indications of tension, or because it is so long since he experienced a true state of calm that any substantial drop in tension *seems* like relaxation to him. Use of the subjective anxiety scale (p. 73) decreases the likelihood of misinformation of this type and perhaps continuous GSR or electromyogram recordings would practically obviate it. Meanwhile, one usually has to rely on careful questioning of the patient to ascertain the true state of affairs. If relaxation is inadequate the therapist must intensify his efforts to improve it either by further instruction or by the introduction of carbon dioxide or drugs (see Chapter 7).

There are other patients who experience difficulty in relaxing as part of a general fear of "letting go". Some of these do make an effort to relax their muscles and may perhaps succeed to an extent; but remain afraid. The autonomic components of the anxiety response remain unchanged and may even increase. The solution to this difficulty varies with the case. Sometimes it is possible to achieve a basis for desensitization simply by telling the patient to be calm and get comfortable in his own way, without attempting to "let himself go". In other cases, one may attempt prior desensitization of the fear of letting go by an *in vivo* method (see below). In yet others, one may resort to one or other of the electrical methods of counteracting anxiety, such as "anxiety-relief" or the recently introduced nonaversive sensory interference technique (see Chapter 8); and sometimes "surrender" to carbon dioxide (Chapter 7) does the trick.

2. *Misleading or Irrelevant Hierarchies*

Even when his hierarchies have none of the faults of conception or construction that may be imputed to elementary errors, there are occasions when the therapist may find himself making no headway, and this is usually because his hierarchies are off the track. Sometimes he has been misled by the patient relating his fears to contexts that are the setting for the fear responses but are not their source. For example, after a man had been treated for twenty sessions with minimal benefit for claustrophobia and agoraphobia (among other hierarchies) it was found that both were based upon a central fear of dying. The patient was anxious either when his freedom of movement was restricted or when he was far from a haven, because both situations implied difficulty in getting help if he should collapse. (During the same period another male patient with a very similar range of phobias was responding to desensitization in classical fashion—for, in his case, the space stimuli were the true antecedents of anxiety.)

There is also a type of neurosis that yields hierarchies that are not amenable to desensitization. In some married women, apparently simple phobias, usually agoraphobia or fear of being alone, that have originated in the course of the marriage, turn out to be fear reactions generalized from an aspect of the marriage that evokes tension and aversion. Seven such cases have been reported by Fry (1962). These phobias may be regarded as true *symbolic* reactions if the word "symbolic" is understood to refer to a stimulus that evokes the same internal response as another stimulus (Osgood, 1953) (see p. 7). *It is quite possible that the discovery of some cases having this unusual feature is what led Freud to the presumption that all phobias have a hidden "real" source.*

An example of this kind of phobia is provided by a 34-year-old woman whose primary complaint was of a feeling of being closed in and an intolerable urge to escape when engaged in conversations with adults—except interchanges on the most casual plane, such as asking the time. This reaction had begun 8 years previously during the patient's first pregnancy. At the commencement of her conditioning therapy no satisfactory precipitating cause of the neurosis could be discovered. She was trained in relaxation and the phobic stimuli taken at their face value. The first hierarchy employed was based on the theme of being stared at, the patient's reactions increasing with the proximity of the starer. The scenes presented to her imagination aroused very little anxiety until a distance of 15 ft was reached—and then there was a *severe* reaction. Various other dimensions were then tried, including *number* of people at a distance, *age* of starer, duration of stare and intensity of illumination—in each instance with the same consequences. It was obvious that something was being missed, but this could not be identified. The case was about to be abandoned when the patient, whom tranquilizers had helped but little asked, "Is there *nothing* that could diminish my distress?" The therapist replied, "At times of special stress you might try a little alcohol." After a long pause she said, "My husband doesn't let me drink." This was the first time she had made an adverse remark about him, but it was the thin end of a wedge that prised open long-suppressed anger and frustration at his absolute domination over every one of her activities. The first pregnancy had precipitated the neurosis because it had seemed to block forever a way out of the marriage—which to the outer world and partly to herself she had represented as a great success.

The phobia now appeared to be primarily a fear of others peering or prying. The impulse to get away from these situations summated with the claustrophobic feeling chronically engendered by the marriage. Thus, an unacknowledged life situation was the real basis of the phobia. But in case the reader should conclude that in *this* case psychoanalysis would have been the treatment of choice, he must be told that the patient had already undergone a psychoanalysis for 2 years without any benefit. The above-mentioned crucial aspects of the marital situation had not emerged during its course, in which, it appears, major attention was focused on oedipal attitudes and the like. The more circumstantial tenets of psychoanalytic theory are often actually a strait-jacket that prohibits the full exploration of a patient's conditioning history. The subsequent handling of this case centred on the use of assertive training.

3. *Inadequacies of Imagery*

Most patients are able to project themselves into imagined anxiety-generating situations in a way that evokes something of the reality of the situations and a corresponding amount of anxiety. The authors have each found this to be the case in about 90 per cent of both South African and American patients. One of us (J. W.), in a limited experience during a year spent in England, gained the impression that the percentage may be considerably lower there, and some recent comments by Meyer (1963) are in line with this impression. The point is far from established; but it is tempting to speculate that the traditional English unbringing that encourages underplaying manifestations of feeling might tend to detach emotions from images.

There are a few people who are simply unable to conjure up either visual or auditory images—at any rate in response to the requirements of the therapist. Far more commonly, the trouble is that while images can be formed they have no sense of reality for the patient. Occasionally, action taken by the therapist leads to the difficulty being overcome. The action is of various kinds—providing much verbal detail of the situation to be imagined, inducing a "deep" trance in good hypnotic subjects, or getting the patient to describe what he imagines. But, usually, such efforts are without avail; and therapeutic change must then depend upon the use of real stimuli.

We have known rare patients who could visualize productively until reaching a certain high point in the hierarchy, when they disengaged themselves from the situations they imagined, and viewed them from the standpoint of a spectator. One such patient who had a cleanliness compulsion of an extreme form, based upon a fear of contamination with his own urine, has been reported elsewhere (Wolpe, 1964). When transfer from the imaginary to the real ceased to be effective, a switch was made to desensitization *in vivo* (see Chapter 8), in which relaxation was counterposed to real stimuli; and this made it possible to continue the offensive against his neurosis, recovery from which has now lasted 3 years.

Several variants of systematic desensitization are discussed in Chapter 8.

Results of Systematic Desensitization

It is useful to know how often one may expect to be successful in applying desensitization to cases in which it is appropriate, though to do so tends to foster the erroneous idea that it is a method *sui generis* instead of merely a particular application of a principle. The only published statistical study to date, that by Wolpe (1961) used as its subject matter 39 patients whose case records were extracted in random fashion from the therapist's files by a casual visitor. Many of these patients also had other neurotic habits that were treated by different methods, deemed more appropriate.

The details of the study are tabulated in Table 1 in which outcome of treatment is indicated on a 5-point scale ranging from 4-plus to zero. A 4-plus rating means complete or almost complete freedom from phobic reactions to all situations in the area of the phobia *encountered in actuality*.[1] A 3-plus rating means an improvement of response such that the phobia is judged by the patient to have lost at least 80 per cent of its

[1] There is some independent evidence of similarity of responses to real and imaginal stimuli. Stone (1955) reported this in respect of auditory stimuli, and Barber and Hahn (1964) in respect of pain.

original strength. A zero rating indicates that there is no discernible change. It will be noted that only 4-plus, 3-plus and zero ratings were applicable to the patients in this series.

Table 2 summarizes the data given in Table 1. There were 68 anxiety-response habits among the 39 patients, of whom 19 had multiple hierarchies. The treatment was judged effective in 35 patients. Forty-five of the anxiety-response habits were apparently eliminated (4-plus rating) and 17 more markedly ameliorated (3-plus rating), making 90 per cent in all. It is probable that many of the latter group would have reached a 4-plus level if additional sessions could have been given. In cases 16 and 29 progress had tailed off when sessions were discontinued, but not in any of the others.

Among the failures, cases 8 and 18 were unable to imagine themselves within situations; case 22 could not confine her imagining to the stated scene and repeatedly exposed herself to excessively disturbing images. She was the patient who was later treated with complete success by the conditioned motor response method outlined on p. 146. Case 25 had interpersonal reactions that led to erratic responses and, having experienced no benefit, sought therapy elsewhere.

The mean number of sessions per phobia was 11·2; the median number of sessions given to patients 10·0. It should be noted that a desensitization session usually takes up only part of a $\frac{3}{4}$-hr interview period, and in cases that also have nonphobic neurotic problems there may be other interviews in which a desensitization session does not occur, and these are not included in this tally.

TABLE 1. BASIC CASE DATA[1]

Number, sex, age	Number of sessions	Hierarchy theme	Outcome	Comments
(1) F. 50	62	(a) Claustrophobia (b) Illness and hospitals (c) Death and its trappings (d) Storms (e) Quarrels	++++ ++++ ++++ +++ ++++	
(2) M. 40	6	(a) Guilt (b) Devaluation	++++ ++++	
(3) F. 24	17	(a) Examinations (b) Being scrutinized (c) Devaluation (d) Discord between others	++++ ++++ ++++ ++++	See data on Miss C. (pp. 73, 81)
(4) M. 24	5	Snake-like shapes	++++	
(5) M. 21	24	(a) Being watched (b) Suffering of others (c) "Jealousy" reaction (d) Disapproval	++++ ++++ ++++ ++++	
(6) M. 28	5	Crowds	+++	
(7) F. 21	5	Criticism	++++	
(8) F. 52	21	(a) Being centre of attention (b) Superstitious	0 0	No disturbance during scenes. Was, in fact, not imagining self in situation
(9) F. 25	9	Suffering and death of others	+++	
(10) M. 22	17	Tissue damage in others	++++	

[1] Modified from Wolpe (1961).

(Table 1—*cont.*)

Number, sex, age	Number of sessions	Hierarchy theme	Outcome	Comments
(11) M. 37	13	Actual or implied criticism	++++	
(12) F. 31	15	Being watched working	+++	
(13) F. 40	16	(a) "Suffering" and eeriness (b) Being devalued (c) Failing to come up to expectations	++++ ++++ ++++	This case has been reported in detail, Wolpe (1959)
(14) M. 36	10	(a) Bright light (b) Palpitations	++++ ++++	
(15) M. 43	9	Wounds and corpses	+++	
(16) M. 27	51	(a) Being watched, especially at work (b) Being criticized	+++ ++++	No anxiety at work after treatment. Anxious at times while watched playing cards
(17) M. 33	8	Being watched at golf	+++	
(18) M. 13	8	Talking before audience (stutterer)	0	No imagined scene was ever disturbing
(19) M. 40	7	Authority figures	++++	
(20) M. 23	4	Claustrophobia	++++	

(Table 1—*cont.*)

Number, sex, age	Number of sessions	Hierarchy theme	Outcome	Comments
(21) F. 23	6	(a) Agoraphobia (b) Fear of falling	0 0	Later successfully treated by conditioned motor response (p. 146)
(22) M. 46	19	(a) Being in limelight (b) Blood and death	+++ ++++	
(23) F. 40	20	Social embarrassment	++++	
(24) F. 28	9	Agoraphobia	0	
(25) F. 48	7	Rejection	+++	
(26) M. 28	13	(a) Disapproval (b) Rejection	+++ ++++	
(27) M. 11	6	Authority figures	++++	
(28) M. 26	217	(a) Claustrophobia (b) Criticism (numerous aspects) (c) Trappings of death	++++ +++ } +++ }	Finally overcome completely by use of "flooding" (p. 136)
(29) F. 20	5	Agoraphobia	++++	
(30) M. 68	23	(a) Agoraphobia (b) Masturbation	++++ ++++	
(31) F. 36	5	Being in limelight	++++	
(32) M. 26	17	(a) Illness and death (b) Own symptoms	+++ +++	
(33) F. 44	9	(a) Being watched (b) Elevators	++++ ++++	

(Table 1—*cont.*)

Number, sex, age	Number of sessions	Hierarchy theme	Outcome	Comments
(34) F. 47	17	Intromission into vagina	+++	After 15th session gradual *in vivo* insertion of objects became possible, and subsequently coitus
(35) M. 37	5	(a) Disapproval (b) Rejection	++++ ++++	
(36) F. 32	25	Sexual stimuli	++++	
(37) M. 36	21	(a) Agoraphobia (b) Disapproval (c) Being watched	++++ ++++ ++++	
(38) M. 18	6	(a) Disapproval (b) Sexual stimuli	+++ ++++	Led to overcoming impotence
(39) F. 48	20	(a) Rejection (b) Crudeness of others	++++ ++++	Stutter much improved

TABLE 2. SUMMARY OF DATA OF TABLE 1

Patients	39	
Number of patients responding to desensitization treatment	35	
Number of hierarchies	68	
Hierarchies overcome	45	91% (overcome + markedly improved)
Hierarchies markedly improved	17	
Hierarchies unimproved	6	9%
Total number of desensitization sessions	762	
Mean session expenditure per hierarchy	11·2	
Mean session expenditure per successfully treated hierarchy	12·3	
Median number of sessions per patient	10·0	

CHAPTER 6

The Use of Sexual Responses

THE present chapter concerns the direct use of sexual responses for overcoming anxieties and inhibitions attached to various aspects of sexuality. Since sexual arousal is in itself reciprocally antagonistic to anxiety, sexual responses may be directly used in cases in which anxiety produces a *partial* inhibition of sexual responsiveness.

When anxiety produces a *complete* inhibition of sexual responsiveness, therapy obviously requires *other* anxiety-inhibiting agents. In a particularly complex case described by Lazarus (1965) a sexually inadequate man required assertive training, systematic desensitization (along four dimensions) and adjunctive therapeutic measures to reinstate his potency. One may also employ nonsexual methods to restore sexual function when the emotional disturbance that inhibits sexual responding has a nonsexual source. A case of impotence based on traumatophobia, for example, was treated by systematic desensitization (Wolpe, 1958, case 8). Similarly, many cases of frigidity, including very recalcitrant ones, may be successfully treated by desensitization (Lazarus, 1963).

The following are the most frequently encountered conditions which may be subsumed under the heading "sexual inadequacy in the male".

(a) Complete or almost complete absence of sexual arousal.
(b) Complete or partial inability to *obtain* an erection despite considerable, and even strong, sexual arousal.
(c) Complete or partial inability to *maintain* an erection. Here there is detumescence before, during, or very soon after intromission, without orgasm or ejaculation.

(d) Premature ejaculation.
(e) Retarded ejaculation.
(f) Absence of pleasure in sex, especially ejaculation without sensation.

In a somewhat parallel way, frigid women may be placed on a continuum extending from those to whom all sexual encounters are terrifying to those who find sexual activities mildly unpleasant or meaningless.

Sexual malfunctions in men and women may also be due to organic factors such as nerve lesions, hormonal deficiencies, or structural defects in the reproductive organs. The present discussion is concerned only with the etiology and treatment of sexual inadequacy due to malconditioning of one kind or another.

Individuals may acquire a repertoire of sexual fears and inhibitions through a variety of learning experiences. A study of our pooled records of thirty-six sexually inadequate men has revealed considerable diversity of antecedents which were in some cases relatively simple and in others highly complex. Examples of the former are a 36-year-old man who was sexually adequate until 2 years previously when he suffered a mild coronary thrombosis while engaged in sexual intercourse, and thereafter experienced trepidation at the thought of sexual indulgence, and a 43-year-old man whose sexual powers gradually declined during a prolonged prostatic infection which occasioned much pain and discomfort after sexual activity. Among those with complex etiologies are patients who had sexually disturbed parents who transmitted to their children their own malconditioned attitudes to sex and to anything with sexual implications. A patient who was sexually adequate with prostitutes but not with "respectable women" was the victim of unfortunate discrimination training. Calvinistic parents had taught him that respectable women are asexual and engage in the "abhorrent act" only through personal martyrdom. Some patients recalled having been punished as children for engaging in exploratory sexual behavior. They had been discouraged from asking sexual questions and had been severely upbraided if seen doing anything "sexual" such as fingering their genitals. In one particularly obstinate case, nudity had acquired specially aversive properties because of insistent maternal warnings that blindness would result from gazing at nude persons of the opposite sex.

Adequate sexual functioning depends upon reciprocity between higher (cortical) centers and more primitive centers. Anxiety has an inhibitory effect at both levels and is the most usual causal factor in "psychogenic" sexual inadequacy. Discharges of the autonomic nervous system absolutely determine the character of sexual performance. Penile erection is a parasympathetic function. Discharges of the sympathetic division exert an inhibitory effect on the processes making for erection, and promote ejaculation. Thus, the predominantly sympathetic discharges of anxiety will tend both to inhibit erection and to stimulate ejaculation prematurely. A rational psychotherapeutic program will, therefore, aim to decrease or eliminate the patient's anxiety in the sexual situation. In principle, it would also be helpful to increase parasympathetic activity relative to sexual function, which is sometimes possible by the use of sex hormones (see Chapter 7).

Therapeutic Techniques

The direct use of sexual responses for eliminating anxiety-associated cues attached to sexual participation has mainly been applied to men, although, as shown by the second case illustration below, these methods can also be the basis of overcoming frigidity. In this, as in other contexts, behavior therapy must be adapted to the needs of the individual patient. The following descriptions and illustrative case histories should make this clear.

Since the behavior therapist sees most sexual inadequacies as being rooted in unadaptive anxiety-response patterns, the elimination of anxiety associated with cues attached to sexual participation is naturally the prime target of his therapy. In experimental neuroses sexual responses have been found to be therapeutic (Napalkov and Karas, 1957). But obviously, they are available for use only where the anxiety has produced merely a partial inhibition of sexual responsiveness. The basic strategy is for the patient to approach his partner only as far as pleasurable anticipatory feelings predominate, having made clear to her that she must never explicitly or implicitly press him to go beyond this point. The sexual arousal is thus kept in the ascendant over anxiety, which, on each occasion, consequently undergoes some measure of conditioned inhibition. This promotes a stronger emergence of sexual arousal which, in turn, further inhibits anxiety. With repetition, conditioned inhibition of anxiety is increased until the anxiety response declines to zero.

Where anxiety is focused on coital performance, the patient is at first advised merely to lie next to his partner in a relaxed way and to enjoy contact without thought of intercourse. The cooperation of the partner must have been obtained beforehand, so that she is prepared for a succession of amorous occasions that will reach various points of intimacy short of coitus. The patient is admonished never to attempt anything more than he can do with complete confidence—that is, without anxiety. He is instructed to proceed no further than mild caressing on the first one or two occasions. The decrease in anxiety from one amorous session to the next facilitates the emergence of sexual arousal which, in turn, further inhibits remaining anxieties. Increasingly close approaches to coitus become possible—lying face to face without genital approximation, then superficial contact, then varying degrees of insertion, and finally increasing amounts of movement, as Case 8 illustrates.

In some cases it is a powerful aid to removing the onus of an expected level of performance from the sufferer to inform him that there are several ways besides direct genital contact by which one's partner may attain orgasmic satisfaction and sexual fulfilment; and then to instruct him in the relevant oral, manual and digital manipulations. Proficiency in these not only provides powerful sources of sexual arousal, but also leads to distracting of attention from the sufferer's genital problem through focusing on pleasures being bestowed on his partner. The primary sexual difficulty is overcome without further formal treatment when a couple learn to accept that sexual satisfaction does not necessarily depend on coitus.

In many of our more recent cases of premature ejaculation we have found it profitable to employ a method devised by Dr. James H. Semans (1956). This consists of controlled acts of manual stimulation of the penis by the wife which lead to a progressive increase in the amount of tactile stimulation needed to bring about ejaculation. The technique (which is illustrated in the treatment of case 8 below) is described by Semans as follows:

> If fatigue is present in either partner, he or she should sleep for a brief period of time. After this, love play is begun and progresses to mutual stimulation of the penis and clitoris. Each is instructed to inform the other of the stage of sexual excitement being experienced. When the husband feels a sensation which is, for him, premonitory to ejaculation, he informs his wife and removes her hand until the sensation disappears. Stimulation is begun again and interrupted by the husband when the premonitory sensation returns. By continuing the technique described above, ejaculation can eventually be postponed indefinitely. Both husband and wife are advised that if erection subsides more than temporarily, a brief sleep or postponement of further stimulation is to be preferred to continuing their efforts at that time. Next, each is told separately, and later together, that ejaculation occurs more rapidly with the penis wet than dry. It is necessary, therefore, to use a bland cream or other means to lubricate the penis while the procedure is repeated.

Semans regards clitoral stimulation of the wife as essential for the continuance of her cooperation. In our view it is a matter of individual decision. There are some women who desire it and who may be brought to orgasm by this means. There are others who cooperate eagerly in the constructive effort, and who prefer themselves not to be stimulated at the time, particularly if they do not get satisfactory orgasms from digital stimulation.

Occasionally, one encounters a patient who, because of previous experiences, has acquired anxiety responses to the very presence of women or to a subclass of that sex. Where all women are involved a formal desensitization program is needed. But where there are some who still evoke erotic types of response, the patient is instructed to have as much commerce as possible with these and none other for a time. Affectional and sexual responses may be expected to decondition whatever anxiety has generalized to them, and later the patient is directed progressively to extend the range of his contacts.

Problems of Female Collaboration

We have emphasized that a cooperative sexual partner is indispensable to the success of techniques utilizing sexual responses, and many patients have one readily available. But others are less fortunate. Sometimes we have had to wait many months before the patient has found somebody sufficiently interested in him to be willing to make the efforts and bear the discomforts required for his treatment. Sometimes, although the patient has a wife or other stable partner, she is unable to participate as needed, either because she is contemptuous of her husband's impotence or, more often, because a long history of disappointment and frustration has quenched her amorous responses, and left only a heavy negativity or a dull resentment. In these instances the therapist does all he can to foster her interest. If she is unmoved by her husband's account of the behavior therapy program the therapist should arrange to speak to her himself. Once she can be persuaded to the first steps, if these are early encouraged by signs of success, the rest may be plain sailing, as in case 9. In other cases there is a need to devise a schedule of approaches to raise the woman's threshold of tolerance of the man.

When all reasonable efforts have failed to procure the kind of physical and affectional relationship needed for our therapeutic program we regard it as entirely proper to encourage the husband to seek out another woman who may be more responsive to him. If, through her, his potency is restored, this in itself may ultimately lead to the reconstruction of the marriage; and even if it does not lead to this, he is better off biologically and psychologically to be able to have outside satisfactions than to be doomed to lifelong chastity.

Provided that reasonable safeguards are observed, it is best for a therapeutic extramarital relationship to be conducted with somebody in whom there is some kind of personal interest, but when this is not possible professional help may have to be sought. In New York, accessible to some marriage guidance counsellors is a "pool" of accredited women who sell their services to men with sexual problems. In other cities there seems to be no other recourse than to seek out a prostitute and it is no easy matter for a sensitive man to find one who is both personally appealing and able to muster enough sympathetic interest to participate in the therapeutic program. One patient with a 16-year history of impotence tried about ten prostitutes before he found a warmhearted and considerate one with whose help his sexual anxiety was overcome and his potency restored.

Case 8

Mr. I., a 36-year-old estate agent, had suffered from premature ejaculation ever since the beginning of his coital life at the age of 16. Ejaculation generally occurred within 15 sec of intromission. He had married at 24. His wife, though deriving some satisfaction from digital orgasms, had become increasingly conscious of her incomplete fulfilment, and had in the past 2 years been showing interest in other men. About 18 months previously, Mr. I. had had about twenty-five consultations with a "dynamic" psychiatrist, and though he had found the probing type of approach irritating, his general confidence had been improved by the treatment; but his sexual performance had remained unchanged. He had had three short-lived extramarital affairs, in each of which his sexual performance had been no better than with his wife. He usually felt that he was doing the "chasing" and was being received to some extent on sufferance.

Mr. I.'s Willoughby score was 30, with highest loadings for humiliation, stage fright and being hurt. He lacked assertiveness in relation to people close to him, but not at all in business affairs. A program of assertive training was seen as a secondary but very relevant therapeutic requirement.

Mrs. I., briefly interviewed, expressed great willingness to take part in a behavior therapy program. She stated that digital orgasms satisfied her physically but not emotionally. She felt that even a relatively small degree of prolongation of intromission would enable her to have coital orgasms. She regarded her marriage as very satisfactory in all other respects.

Therapy of the sexual inadequacy based upon use of sexual responses made combined use of two lines of approach: (1) graded penile stimulation by the technique of Semans (see above); and (2) gradual advances towards coitus. Mr. I. kept a detailed record of his performances which he timed as accurately as possible with a bedside clock. The data of the early and middle stages of his record are reproduced below. Each figure refers to *the number of minutes of manual stimulation of the penis by his wife that brought him just short of ejaculation* for each successive sequence of stimulations.

First occasion (Saturday): 8, 6, 6, 6, and 3 min.
Second occasion (Saturday): 11, 7, 3, 4, and 4 min.
Third occasion (Sunday): 8, 6, 5, and 18+ min.
Fourth occasion (Sunday): 17 min.
Fifth occasion (Monday): 33 min. At this juncture he felt confident enough to have Mrs. I. stimulate him as he sat astride her. The time to "pre-ejaculation" on two successive sequences was 2 min and 3 min.
Sixth occasion (Monday): lying face to face sideways the pre-ejaculatory point was reached in 10 min and was maintained for 20 more min, when Mrs. I. desisted because of fatigue. After this occasion Mr. I. declared that he had never before been able to reach and maintain so high a level of excitement; but this became the norm subsequently.
Seventh occasion (Monday): same as sixth occasion but "pre-ejaculation" was reached in 14 min and again maintained to a total of 30 min.
Eighth occasion (Tuesday): same as sixth occasion but "pre-ejaculation" was reached in 12 min and maintained to 30 min.
Ninth occasion (Wednesday): penile stimulation while astride—5, 12+, and 9+ min.
Tenth occasion (Wednesday): penile stimulation while astride—12 and 11 min.
Eleventh occasion (Thursday): penile stimulation while astride—12½, 12 and 23 min. After the last Mr. I. inserted just the glans of his penis into the vagina, maintaining it there for 5 min. In the course of this time Mrs. I. became excited. Thereupon he withdrew and they both had orgasms digitally.
Twelfth occasion (Friday): partial insertion (glans penis) for 20 min during which Mrs. I. alone moved and in this way gradually manipulated the penis deeper. At the end of the period Mr. I. withdrew as he felt ejaculation imminent.

Mr. I. now reported to the therapist that he was feeling very much less anxious than before at partial insertion of his penis. He was finding that his stimulation of his wife was the greatest factor increasing his own excitation.

The next objective was to increase both depth and duration of insertion, and thereafter to add small amounts of movement. In the meantime, at each meeting with the therapist the patient was receiving training in progressive relaxation.

Thirteenth occasion (Friday evening after meeting with therapist): partial intercourse lasted 30 min—partial insertion 80 per cent of the time and full insertion about 20 per cent, for about a minute at a time. During this minute Mr. I. would move constantly, without feeling any danger of ejaculation, but when Mrs. I. moved five to ten times ejaculation would become imminent.

Fourteenth occasion (Saturday): partial intercourse as above, 23 min and then Mr. I. ejaculated during an attempt to reverse positions.

Fifteenth occasion (Saturday): fifteen minutes, much the same as the thirteenth occasion.

Sixteenth occasion (Sunday): ejaculated after 4 min.

Seventeenth occasion (Monday): forty minutes, varying between one-quarter to half insertion of penis. Ejaculation was several times imminent, but Mr. I. averted it by relaxing each time.

Now the therapist directed Mr. I. to concentrate first on prolonging full intromission, and then gradually to introduce movement, but preventing excessive excitation by avoiding stimulation of Mrs. I. He was told always to keep well within his capacity to control. After a few minutes of this it would be permissible to go on to orgasm, emphasizing, during this, clitoral pressure by the penis.

Eighteenth occasion (Monday): orgasm after 15 min of complete insertion with small movements.

Nineteenth occasion: orgasm after 29 min of small movements. Mrs. I. said that she too had been on the point of orgasm.

Further sexual occasions enabled gradually increasing excursions of movement, and finally, a major breakthrough occurred after the thirteenth therapeutic occasion. Mr. I. retained his erection while Mrs. I. had four orgasms, and he ejaculated during the last of them. From this time onward there was mutually satisfactory sexual performance that gradually improved. There were fourteen therapeutic interviews in all over 5 weeks. Mr. I.'s Willoughby score at the last interview was 13.

Case 9

Mrs. W., aged 24 years, who had been married for 18 months, complained that she had never obtained sexual satisfaction and that for the past year had invariably experienced such violent dyspareunia that coitus had become insufferable. She was both grateful and troubled at the fact that her husband had made no sexual advances for the past 5 months. She felt that "things can't go on like this", but was filled with trepidation at the idea of resuming sexual relations. Further discussion revealed that her husband suffered from premature ejaculation. Mrs. W. was nevertheless convinced that her inability to obtain sexual satisfaction was entirely her own fault. She had grown more tense and upset with each successive sexual failure until the eventual impasse.

Her husband, a 28-year-old engineer, was interviewed. He agreed that he tended to ejaculate almost immediately after intromission. His sexual ineptitude had caused him to denigrate himself at all levels, although he was in fact adequate at his work and in social relationships.

At a joint interview with Mr. and Mrs. W., the therapist instructed them to resume love-making, but to proceed no further than kissing and caressing. A week later they were advised to extend their range of physical attentions but never to proceed beyond the point where *both* remained entirely at ease and free from anxiety. They were informed that the act of coitus should not be attempted until both had attained manually induced orgasms. In his wife's presence Mr. W. was told how to induce an orgasm by manual stimulation of the vulva, vagina and clitoris.

Their pattern of love-play during the next 2½ weeks was confined to heavy petting while in the nude, Mr. W. obtaining sexual relief through manual stimulation by his wife. Mrs. W. was, however, at this stage averse to manual stimulation as a means to orgasm. They were therefore instructed to bide their time until Mrs. W. felt fully ready. This transpired within a month, and soon both were enjoying orgasms through manual stimulation.

The following love-making sequence was then proposed: they would kiss and caress as usual and Mrs. W. would satisfy her husband manually. Mr. W. would then apply manual stimulation to his wife. If he became rearoused during the course of this intimacy, they would have coitus. It was impressed upon them, however, that Mrs. W. was to achieve sexual satisfaction "one way or the other". Mr. W. soon discovered that he was able to delay ejaculation almost indefinitely "the second time round".

Over some 3–4 months this couple developed a well formulated sexual sequence. First there was mutual masturbation to the point of orgasm, which Mrs. W. came to achieve very rapidly. After a brief rest, they would resume love-play, become aroused again and have coitus which usually culminated in orgasms for both. The attainment of mutual *coital* satisfaction hinged on the fact that Mrs. W.'s new-found positive responses (emanating from digital orgasms) enabled them to discover that Mr. W. was able to delay ejaculation during coitus. Success made Mr. W. a more proficient lover, enhancing their mutual pleasure.

This couple have now enjoyed a full and happy sex life for over 5 years.

Results of Treatment of Sexual Inadequacy by Use of Sexual Responses

Table 3 presents a collection from our combined files of cases whose impotence or premature ejaculation was treated by manipulating sexual situations so that sexual responses were as far as possible kept dominant over anxiety. We have included all the cases we could find, but one or two of the early records could not be located. The findings are summarized in Table 4. In all, there were 31 cases. Of these, 21 (67·7 per cent) achieved entirely satisfactory sexual performance, and 6 (19·4 per cent) others were enabled to function at a level sufficiently improved to be acceptable to their sexual partners. The mean time to the final result was 11·5 weeks, and the median 8·0 weeks.

TABLE 3. CASES OF IMPOTENCE TREATED BY RECIPROCAL INHIBITION OF ANXIETY BY SEXUAL RESPONSES

Patient number	Age	Time span of active *in vivo* "campaign" (weeks)	Outcome
1	53	3	Recovered with new consort. Previously no benefit in 12 weeks with un-cooperative consort
2	31	1	Recovered
3	40	8	Recovered
4	46	10	Recovered
5	46	20	Recovered
6	40	4	Recovered
7	41	12 (intermittent and furtive)	Much improved
8	50	6	Recovered but no transfer to wife

(Table 3—*cont.*)

Patient number	Age	Time span of active *in vivo* "campaign" (weeks)	Outcome
9	49	2	Recovered (major factor removal of impregnation anxiety by Enovid)
10	20	6	Recovered (major factor was resolution of fears about masculinity induced by psychoanalytic reading)
11	49	10	Improved from almost complete erectile failure to functionally sufficient erections to make marriage possible and to satisfy and impregnate wife
12	35	6	Markedly improved at time when therapist left country. Appropriate assertion towards wife major factor
13	36	5	Recovered (case 8)
14	44	16 (infrequent opportunities)	Unimproved. No apparent sexual anxiety. Hypersensitivity of glans
15	40	9	Recovered (details in Wolpe, in Eysenck 1960, p. 110)
16	35	8 (preceded by 12 weeks of overcoming interpersonal fears)	Improved from no erection to strong ones. Coitus improving when therapist left country
17	32	50 (very irregular, various women)	Unimproved
18	18	66 (very irregular opportunities at first)	Recovered

(Table 3—*cont.*)

Patient number	Age	Time span of active *in vivo* "campaign" (weeks)	Outcome
19	39	12	Recovered. At first erections only possible with aid of testosterone
20	19	13	Recovered
21	27	2	Improved (a rather effeminate man who had been completely impotent with each of his three wives who had each rejected and divorced him because of his sexual disabilities. He had had almost 18 years of psychoanalysis. At the end of behavior therapy he was potent only when his wife assumed the "on top" position)
22	28	15	Recovered (case 9)
23	32	3	Recovered (major factor was acceptance of the fact that if he failed to satisfy his wife during coitus, it was perfectly "normal" and in no way "perverted" to bring her to orgasm digitally)
24	32	10 (preceded by 14 weeks of assertive training and desensitization to fears of illness)	Much improved
25	23	4	Recovered (major factor was increased self-confidence through acquiring an adequate repertoire of love-making techniques)
26	20	3	Recovered (major factor was the realization that sexual intercourse does not weaken one)

(Table 3—*cont.*)

Patient number	Age	Time span of active *in vivo* "campaign" (weeks)	Outcome
27	52	8	Unimproved
28	34	18	Improved from premature ejaculations with an almost flaccid penis to a stage where he brought his wife to coital orgasm about 50 per cent of the time
29	39	5	Improved from total lack of erections to the ability to have successful coitus upon awakening in the mornings
30	34	22	Unimproved
31	43	3	Improved, but always relied on "a stiff drink" before coitus

TABLE 4

Number of cases	Entirely satisfactory functional results (recovered or much improved)	Limited but significant functional improvement	Failures
31	21 (67·7%)	6 (19·4%)	4 (12·9%)

Mean age: 36·3 years.
Mean time span: 11·5 weeks.
Median time span: 8·0 weeks.
Median time span for recovered and much-improved cases: 6·0 weeks.

CHAPTER 7

Drugs, Carbon Dioxide and Abreaction

THESE topics are grouped together because they involve procedures in which the therapist does not have the specific control of stimuli and responses that characterizes most behavior therapy techniques.

The Use of Drugs

Symptomatic Uses

When a patient suffers more or less continuously from a considerable amount of emotional disturbance it is usually desirable to administer some drug or combination of drugs that will make him reasonably comfortable. As any experienced clinician knows, it is always a matter of trial and error to determine which drugs are effective in any individual. In our hands, meprobamate (400 mg) three or four times a day, dexamyl (drinamyl) one to two tablets morning and midday, and librium (10–20 mg) three times a day have all been useful, and it has been our practice to try them first. When none of these has succeeded we have been willing to try any of a considerable number of other drugs—chlorpromazine, compazine, stelazine, atarax, ethchlorvynol (placidyl). We have at times also used various antidepressants, such as parnate and nardil, on the strength of Sargant and Dally's report (1962) of their effectiveness in relieving the emotional symptoms of many cases of neurosis. It is unusual for anxiety to be *entirely* removed by drugs in the usual doses.

We have, however, never known these drugs to be inimical to the achievement of the fundamental changes sought through behavior therapy, and there is little doubt that in some cases they have even promoted these changes (see below). The hazard of addiction is small when the duration of drug treatment is limited. Usually, as the neurotic reactions are deconditioned the dosages required become less, and it is often possible to dispense with drugs a good while before the conclusion of therapy.

Drugs may also be beneficially administered to overcome the anxieties evoked by specific situations. For example, a patient who has a fear of "public scrutiny" may take a tranquilizing preparation an hour before making a speech, and one who has a fear of flying may do the same before a journey by air. Many patients discover that they can protect themselves against special anxiety sources in this way.

Symptomatic control of specific syndromes by drugs has also been reported. Imipramine has controlled enuresis (Destounis, 1963) and encopresis (Abraham, 1963). Systematic use of the drug can achieve what Drooby (1964) has called a "reliable truce" with certain disabilities when attempts at reconditioning are impracticable or unsuccessful. Drooby found that enuresis ceased completely or almost completely in a matter of days in every one of forty-five children to whom he administered imipramine (25 mg) two or three times a day according to age. The treatment was not curative, for when the drug was withheld enuresis recurred. However, when the effects of withdrawing the drug were tested after a year of use, 30 per cent of the subjects remained free from enuresis—the same percentage as in a control group. If a child and his parents can be spared the inconvenience of wet beds without impeding the development of whatever processes underlie recovery, it is obviously worth while to employ drugs, particularly when circumstances preclude treatment by the bell-and-blanket method (Jones, 1960; Lovibond, 1963).

Drooby (1965) has also successfully used imipramine and other drugs such as thioridazine (mellaril), diazepam (valium), and phenelzine (nardil) (each sometimes in combination with ergotamine) to curb anxiety and delay ejaculation in cases of premature ejaculation. A number of reports confirming his experience have been published by others (e.g. Singh, 1963). It appears that the repeated successful performance of sexual intercourse under the influence of these drugs sometimes enables the patient to perform satisfactorily without them (see p. 119). The inhibition of a large measure of anxiety by a drug presumably makes it possible for the sexual arousal to effect the reciprocal inhibition of whatever anxiety remains. It is similarly possible to achieve a "truce" with such symptoms as stuttering, as shown, for example, in the "good" or "very good" effects achieved by the use of meprobamate in thirteen out of eighteen patients treated by Maxwell and Paterson (1958).

Adjuvant Uses of Drugs

Various chemical substances may be used to promote relaxation when all efforts at active relaxation fail to produce sufficient calmness for desensitization. They may also be used when, for the same reason, desensitization is proceeding too slowly. When ongoing anxiety is due to specific external stimuli or thought contents, a drug, such as one of the tranquilizers named above, may be prescribed to be taken an hour or two before the interview. But where the anxiety is of the pervasive, "free-floating" type (i.e. anxiety that is apparently conditioned to pervasive aspects of stimulation, such as space, time, bodily sensations, etc.) by far the most effective measure consists of administering to the patient one to four single full-capacity inhalations of a mixture of carbon dioxide and oxygen (see p. 121).

From time to time reports appear in the literature on the beneficial use of male sex hormone in the treatment of cases of impotence (e.g. Miller, Hubert and Hamilton, 1938). One of us (J. W.) has, in the course of 16 years of psychotherapeutic practice, twice succeeded in augmenting a very low sexual drive in males by daily injections of testosterone, to an extent that sexual performance became possible and subsequently continued without further use of hormone.

The Use of Drugs for Specific Deconditioning

From various reports published during the last half-century, both in Russia (e.g. Pavlov, 1941) and in the United States (Dworkin, Raginsky and Bourne, 1937; Masserman and Yum, 1946), it is evident that lasting recovery or improvement may be procured in neurotic animals by keeping them under the influence of such sedative drugs as bromides, barbiturates, or alcohol for long periods. It would appear, although it is not always specifically stated in the reports, that at various times while under the influence of the drugs the animals were exposed to the stimuli conditioned to the neurotic reaction. But none of the experimenters deliberately and systematically brought the stimuli into play as an essential part of the therapeutic action.

This was done for the first time in a study reported by Miller, Murphy and Mirsky (1957). Using electric shock as the unconditioned stimulus, they conditioned four groups of rats to perform an avoidance response at the presentation of a buzzer. For the purpose of studying extinction of the avoidance response under different conditions the animals in two of the groups received injections of saline, and those of the other two groups injections of chlorpromazine on each of 4 consecutive days. One of the two saline-injected groups (Group I) and one of the two chlorpromazine-injected groups (Group II) received fifteen unreinforced presentations of the buzzer on each of the 4 days, while the animals of the other two groups were simply returned to the living cage after receiving their injections. During these 4 days Group II animals made far fewer avoidance responses (less than 5 per cent of trials) than Group I (more than 70 per cent of trials). On the fifth and subsequent days, when all groups were given unreinforced trials *without receiving any further injections*, Group II manifested a much lower percentage of avoidance responses than any of the other groups. Whereas the other groups showed an average of about 60 per cent avoidance responses, Group II showed only about 20 per cent; and in eleven of the fifteen animals that comprised the group the level did not go above that observed during the 4 days under the influence of the drug. That this lasting therapeutic effect was related to the autonomic action of the chlorpromazine and not to the suppression of motor responses was indicated by repeating the experiment with phenobarbitone in a dosage that had previously been equated with chlorpromazine in terms of motor retardation effects. In the animals given phenobarbitone the level of avoidance responses after stopping the drug was not diminished. It is crucial to note that the chlorpromazine has lasting effects only if, in the authors' words, "the opportunity for relearning is afforded during the administration of the agent".

It is reasonable to assume that reciprocal inhibition was the mechanism of this relearning. The animals were, through earlier conditioning, capable of responding also to other stimuli in the environment besides the buzzer. But without the "protection" of the chlorpromazine the avoidance response to the buzzer was overwhelmingly strong. In animals who had been given chlorpromazine any remnant of the avoidance response (and the concomitant anxiety) could be reciprocally inhibited by whatever other responses were being produced by other stimuli in the environment. Obviously this explanation calls for systematic study; but some support is given to it by Berkun's observation (1957) that animals in whom *weak* anxiety-cum-avoidance responses have been conditioned can overcome these responses by mere exposure, first to situations similar to those associated with the original conditioning, and then to the original situation itself.

The important clinical possibilities suggested by the Miller, Murphy and Mirsky experiment have hardly been probed. Winkelman (1954) studied patients to whom chlorpromazine had been administered for 6 months or more in doses sufficient to obtain marked diminution of neurotic symptoms, after which the drug was gradually withdrawn. He found that improvement persisted for at least 6 months after the withdrawal in 35 per cent of the patients. However, there was no control study to show what would have happened to patients given a placebo instead of chlorpromazine. We have observed a number of patients who have responded so well to such drugs as chlorpromazine, meprobamate, or codeine that exposure to situations ordinarily disturbing has not elicited the expected disturbance. If the drug is administered consistently for a period of weeks or months so that no significant anxiety is ever produced, exposure to the situation upon discontinuing the drug elicits notably less anxiety than before. For example, the ordinarily severe classroom anxiety experienced by a student was markedly ameliorated by meprobamate. After receiving adequate doses of the drug on every school day for 6 weeks, a drug-free test showed the anxiety to be diminished by an estimated 40 per cent. The reintroduction of the drug for a further 6 weeks led to a further 30 per cent decrement of anxiety level in the classroom after the drug was again withdrawn—an overall improvement of about two-thirds. Among the cases of stuttering treated by meprobamate in the Maxwell and Paterson study (1958) mentioned above was that of a 25-year-old butcher who was eventually able to dispense with the drug "and still maintain a marked speech improvement". Clearly, if the neuroses of a substantial percentage of patients could be cured by judicious use of a program of anxiety control by drugs, an enormous saving of therapist time would be accomplished. One point that must be emphasized is that the effectiveness of such programs probably depends greatly upon insuring that high anxiety evocation never occurs; for, whenever it does, it may be expected to recondition a substantial degree of anxiety and lose hard-won ground.

Carbon Dioxide–Oxygen

The method of treating pervasive anxiety is not that of Meduna, by which the patient inhales a mixture of 30 per cent carbon dioxide and 70 per cent oxygen until he loses consciousness, but that of La Verne (1953), in which a stronger mixture is inhaled, one breath at a time. The mixture that has become standard consists of 65 per cent carbon dioxide and 35 per cent oxygen;

but a cylinder of 40 per cent carbon dioxide and 60 per cent oxygen should be available for those patients for whom the higher concentration is found to be irritating or excessively drastic in its effects.

The technical details are as follows. The therapist first ascertains the level of the patient's anxiety in terms of subjective units of disturbance (suds) (see page 73). He then tells the patient what he proposes to do and what the probable effects will be. The exact manner of presentation varies, but a fairly typical speech is the following.

> It would obviously be a good thing if we could facilitate the effects of muscle relaxation. We sometimes find that we can get a good deal of help from inhaling a mixture of carbon dioxide and oxygen. Carbon dioxide and oxygen are physiological gases that we always have in our bodies. Carbon dioxide stimulates the breathing—and as a matter of fact, it is frequently used to revive patients under anesthesia. Now, in these cylinders, there is a concentration of carbon dioxide that is much higher than that which you normally have in your lungs. I am going to ask you to inhale the gas mixture through this mask when I have filled the bag—one breath at a time. After a delay of a few seconds you will begin to notice certain symptoms which are unusual but not really unpleasant. You will notice that you become short of breath, that your heart quickens, your face flushes and your extremities tingle. You may become rather dizzy, and possibly also have some other sensations. These reactions will reach a peak in about five seconds, and subside in another five seconds or so.
>
> Now this is what I want you to do. Take the mask in your hand. Watch as I fill the bag with the mixture of gases. (*Pause while the bag is filled.*) In a few seconds I am going to ask you to do the following things. First, empty your lungs—breath out as far as you can. Then apply the mask over your nose and chin quite firmly. Then press this button on top of the mask, which releases the gas, and mainly through your mouth breathe in until you have about half-filled your lungs with the gas. After this, remove the mask from your face.

In some cases it is found that even half-filling the lungs with the gas mixture produces a substantial respiratory reaction; in others little or no effect is produced; in still others the reaction is small and insufficient. It is desirable initially not to fill the lungs completely, because a few patients are greatly disturbed by the unusual sensations brought forth by the gas mixture. It is very important in all cases to inquire beforehand whether the patient has any fears of suffocation or of anesthetics. In the case of those that do, a very slow and careful approach should be made to this method of treatment, devoting to an "habituation program" a few minutes of each of several successive sessions. At first the patient may be asked to do nothing more than handle the mask; then he may sniff it cautiously while the gas mixture flows through the opened valve; then he may take a short sniff out of the full bag; and thereafter increasingly deep breaths until he eventually inhales fully. A few individuals are so distressed by the sensations produced that it never becomes possible for carbon dioxide to be profitably employed on them.

Unless the mixture produces a marked respiratory reaction it is unusual to find any significant lowering of the level of anxiety. When even a full-capacity inhalation fails to elicit hyperventilation, the requisite response can often be obtained by asking the patient to hold his breath for as long as he can after inhaling.

After each inhalation the therapist obtains from the patient a statement of the level of his anxiety, and notes the effects by the convenient notation illustrated in the following example:

Carbon dioxide–oxygen (× 5) 60 — 45 — 35 — 25 — 20 — 20 (suds).

The fact that the score stayed at 20 was an indication that no further lowering of the anxiety level could be expected, and therefore administrations of the gas mixture were ended. While this is not ideal, it is self-evident that the patient's efforts at relaxation are far more likely to reduce the anxiety level to zero from 20 suds than from 60 suds.

The mechanism of the anxiety-reducing effects of carbon dioxide–oxygen mixtures is not known. It has been suggested (Wolpe, 1958) that it is based upon reciprocal inhibition of anxiety either by the responses produced by the gas, or by the post-inhalation state of relaxation, or, possibly, upon both. No formal studies have been made to date. All that seems reasonably certain is that the effect is not a direct pharmacological one dependent upon the presence of carbon dioxide in the body; for, clearly, any surfeit of the gas is dissipated in a matter of minutes; yet one or two inhalations may remove pervasive anxiety for weeks (Wolpe, 1958), though much more often the anxiety reappears in a matter of hours. A conditioning hypothesis is thoroughly consonant with this. Exposure to a specific anxiety-evoking stimulus situation is always required to re-establish the pervasive anxiety that has been removed by the inhalations; and if the patient rarely encounters such situations, he may be free from pervasive anxiety for long periods. We believe, as stated above, that this anxiety becomes conditioned to pervasive aspects of environments in certain individuals. We shall continue to be ignorant of the exact conditioning processes involved until the necessary investigations are done.

Abreaction (with and without Drugs)

An abreaction may be defined as the re-evocation, with strong emotional accompaniment, of a fearful past experience. Some abreactions are followed by therapeutic changes, while others are not, and many even leave the patient worse off than before. If we could induce abreaction at will and also predict which individuals would respond favorably we should be able vastly to expedite therapy in many cases. At present the induction of abreaction is unreliable and its effects so unpredictable that it is not our policy to attempt it unless we fail to make satisfactory progress with the usual procedures whose effects we can control and whose mechanisms we more clearly understand. It would seem, however, that in a certain percentage of neurotic patients the unadaptive emotional responses have been conditioned at the outset to particularly intricate stimulus compounds which cannot be adequately replaced by stimulus situations extracted from the present. Then abreaction may be wellnigh indispensable as suggested by Wolpe (1958, p. 198) and again by Costello (1964).

The therapeutic efficacy of an abreaction, judging from Grinker and Spiegel's experiences (1945) with war neuroses, bears no relation to the previous *accessibility* to recall of the abreacted experience. On the evidence, the one apparent essential is for the abreaction to take place in a protected setting such as the psychotherapeutic relationship affords (Grinker and Spiegel, 1945). This consideration was the basis for Wolpe's (1958) suggestion that the therapeutic effects obtained during abreaction represent a special case of the nonspecific effects that occur in a proportion of the cases receiving any form of psychotherapy. The essence of the matter seems to be a function of reciprocal inhibition of anxiety by othero emtional responses induced in the patient by the therapeutic situation.

Abreactions take place without the use of drugs in a number of different ways. Sometimes they arise unbidden, during history-taking or during attempts at systematic desensitization. A truck driver had, following an accident, a marked phobia for driving (in addition to considerable pervasive anxiety). After training in relaxation and the construction of a hierarchy on the theme of driving, he was asked, during his first desensitization session, to imagine himself sitting at the wheel of a car that was stationary and whose engine was not running. He suddenly began to verbalize the details of the accident, broke into a sweat and became very agitated. After about a minute, when the reaction subsided, he was asked to open his eyes. When he did so he appeared tired but relieved, and said that he was no longer afraid to drive a truck. The test of reality proved him right. Another example of unscheduled abreaction occurred in a 50-year-old lawyer who had been vaguely tense for decades, and who had come for treatment mainly because of increasing insomnia. During instruction in assertive behavior, he began to talk of his childhood, and mentioned that though his family had been very poor he would never take anything from other people. He recounted an incident at school when, being a good athlete, he had taken part in a race and had been the only contestant without spiked shoes because he had refused to accept them from the school. He became very tearful during this narrative. At the next interview, a week later, he said that he was feeling better and that his duration of sleep had gone up from 4 to 6 hr per night. At this interview he abreacted to a story concerning a friend in the Army towards whom he had been aggressive and who had been killed within a month. Further but smaller abreactions were subsequently induced deliberately to this same situation under hypnosis. Each of these abreactions was followed by a signal improvement. Augmented by assertive training and by desensitization to receiving praise and favors, they led to an apparently complete recovery in a total of fifteen sessions.

High emotional arousal is also sometimes therapeutic when set off by strongly fearful stimuli *rooted in the present*. It is not unlikely that this will ultimately prove to be parallel in all respects to the classical abreaction involving past events. The essential procedure is to expose the patient, either in imagination or in reality, to present situations that can arouse intense anxiety (see section on "stimulus flooding", Chapter 8).

If the therapist has decided to try to bring about an abreaction, there are several courses open to him. He may employ one of the methods mentioned above—endeavoring to plunge the patient, either with or without hypnosis, into some situation *known* to be highly disturbing. He may also try to gain access to unknown material by asking the hypnotized patient to create a fantasy on unpleasant or fearful events out of the past. This may be aided by the "age-regression" technique in which the therapist suggests to the person that he is returning to past ages of his life, which start at a relatively recent date and then go back year by year. We have used this technique occasionally, and at times with some success, but have not seen the dramatic effects reported by others.

The most easily applicable methods of pursuing abreactions involve drugs. The first of these to gain widespread interest was pentobarbitone (pentothal), whose use in this manner was introduced by Horsley (1936) and employed during World War II. At this time, and for a few years following, the drug was occasionally used by J. W. in the hope of obtaining beneficial abreactions; but though abreactions did occur fairly often, and were at times very vivid and colorful, in not a single case did unequivocal and lasting benefit ensue. It would seem that drugs that *elevate* arousal should be more likely to lead to abreactions. The most effective substances have so far been di-ethyl ether (in its exciting phase) and lysergic acid. The amphetamines (notably methedrine) can also produce abreactions, but it has not been evident from the reports we have perused that these yield any lastingly beneficial after-effects; and sometimes (as has been our own experience) sensitization is afterwards found to have been increased. Possibly, the amphetamines too greatly favor responses of the sympathetic division of the autonomic nervous system.

For a full description of the technique of obtaining excitatory abreaction with ether the reader should consult the original accounts by Palmer (1944) and by Shorvon and Sargant (1947). While the patient lies on his back on a couch the therapist talks to him informally about events that preceded the incident on which it is hoped the patient will abreact. The ether-soaked mask is held a few inches from the face, and then rather rapidly approximated. In a matter of minutes the patient becomes excited, and in a successful case begins to recite the events that led to the precipitation of his neurosis. He is encouraged to "cry, shout and struggle"; and it is, of course, very desirable to have an assistant at hand to restrain excessive movement. Shorvon and Sargant express the dominating opinion when they state that one is much more likely to produce emotional release in an individual suffering from a recent traumatic neurosis than in one with a longstanding illness. But even with recent cases, as they also point out, there are many failures. An interesting case was recently described by Little and James (1964), in which a neurosis originating in battle 15 years previously was progressively overcome in five sessions of ether abreactions. During the course of these abreactions the patient pieced together the tremendously disturbing sequence of events that had precipitated the neurosis, beginning with his shooting of two young German captors while the three of them were in a ditch taking shelter from artillery shells.

Lysergic acid diethylamide (LSD 25) was introduced into psychiatry because of its ability to promote vivid imagery and striking emotional responses. Beneficial abreactions have frequently been reported (e.g. Sandison, 1954) but the therapeutic effects have been variable. It is only recently (Costello, 1964) that a deliberate attempt has been made to channel the course of events set off by the drug in accordance with conditioning principles. Costello reported three cases with which he achieved rapid recovery and one may hope that his technique will prove to be a convenient means of procuring beneficial abreaction.

The details are as follows. The patient is given orally 400 mg of LSD in water—a higher dose than that given by many therapists. Costello states: "Experience with the drug in Saskatchewan has suggested that higher doses make it almost impossible for the patient to 'fight' the drug effect, thus producing better therapeutic results." The patient goes through the first stage described by Blewett and Chwelos (1959), consisting mainly of perceptual disturbance and symptoms like palpitations and nausea, while being offered reassurance and soothing music. This seems to make more acceptable the second stage of confusion, due to the flooding of consciousness with ideas and visual images, which arrives after an hour or two. Costello describes the sequence of events in his first case (a woman with a 16-year history of claustrophobia with religious undertones) from stage 2 onwards as follows:

> When she reported that she was getting vivid visual images, part of Offenbach's Gaîté Parisienne was played, followed closely by some spirituals sung by Mahalia Jackson. During the Mahalia Jackson record the patient became quite agitated. The volume was turned down and the patient was told to face whatever ideas, thoughts or pictures were presenting themselves to her. She was told that life was a beautiful though sometimes awesome pattern which we spoiled by turning away from it. Thus stage 4 of the experience (ordering of the perceptions) was suggested to the patient. The patient at this point stretched out her hand for me to hold and held my hand tightly. After a few seconds she loosened her hold on my hand, became very relaxed and said, "And I was afraid." I agreed there was nothing whatsoever to be afraid of and

once again put the Gaîté Parisienne record on. The patient almost immediately began to laugh. Then she said "sex", laughed more and then said, "I was going to be a nun." This was followed by more laughter. The Mahalia Jackson record was then played and the patient lay on the settee looking extremely relaxed. For the rest of the session, until 3.00 p.m., the patient listened to music, drank coffee occasionally and talked a little about her family, their holidays, her husband's hunting, etc. At no time was her camp experience or her phobic condition discussed. At 3.00 p.m. the patient was given 100 mg sparine intramuscularly. . . .

On the third day the patient was asked to visit me, and at this time reported that she felt very relaxed. She had forgotten a lot of the experience but told me: "There were so many things at the same time . . . my mother . . . and then a boy at high school—he wanted to touch me but I would not dream of it . . . and the priest, and then my mother back again and wanting to be a nun . . . all so fast." The following Sunday the patient went to church, sat in the middle row and "felt so comfortable".

Six months later the patient was interviewed again and reported that she had completely recovered from her claustrophobia, that she was going to more places with her husband, and that she was generally much happier.

What is unusual about Costello's handling of this case and of the others he describes is that he deliberately attempts to displace the emotional reactions of anxiety and distress by joy and tranquility *in the continued presence of the anxiety-evoking stimuli.* Presumably the anxiety could thus be reciprocally inhibited, and the general context of high emotional arousal would make it possible for the anxiety-response habit to be largely or entirely eliminated in the course of even a single session. Costello's article gives the impression that beneficial abreactions are rather easily induced by his routine. If this is so, every psychotherapist will eagerly welcome it. Our own first three attempts have not been successful; but we intend to make further trials.

CHAPTER 8

Additional Techniques[1]

THE previous chapters have in the main described the methods of behavior therapy that are most widely used today. This chapter will present a number of other methods that have been employed in special cases or recently introduced. Several of the latter should at present be considered essentially experimental; but it is not out of the question that one or more of them will ultimately earn preference over some methods in common current use. Certain of these additional techniques are only adjuvant, but the application of others can produce major therapeutic progress. For example, certain patients who have responded poorly to a reassuring relationship, relaxation, assertive training, and systematic desensitization may date gratifying improvement from the introduction of, say, "anxiety relief conditioning".

Methods Involving Concept Control

Correcting Misconceptions, Developing Insight, and Imparting Rational Values and Beliefs

The edifice of psychoanalytic therapy rests on the acquisition of "insight", and an entire system of psychotherapy has been

[1] Most of these techniques are special to behavior therapy, having evolved from the deliberate application of principles of learning. A number of others have in various forms long played a part in the traditional psychotherapies. In behavior therapy they have acquired a character that is in many respects distinctive, being always geared to facilitate the specific reconditioning procedures.

based on the rational correction of the faulty assumptions and illogical philosophies which may underlie maladaptive behavior (Ellis, 1962). Behavior therapists, by contrast, regard rational corrections as, in most instances, merely a background to the specific reconditioning of reactions that usually belong to the autonomic nervous system.

It is often comforting and sometimes helpful to apprehend the origins and development of patients' maladaptive reactions, and to examine and correct faulty attitudes and misperceptions. Significantly, however, Festinger (1964) was unable to find a single experimental investigation which actually showed that a change in cognition led (*per se*) to a change in behavior. Conversely, in keeping with Taylor's (1962) demonstrations that changes in behavior can result in corresponding changes in perception, we have frequently observed patients acquire profound conceptual changes following a successful desensitization program. The correction of misconceptions, however, is often a necessary forerunner to effective desensitization. A patient who expressed undue guilt about the fact that he indulged in masturbation, to which he erroneously attributed his tension headaches, fear of heights and of answering telephones, necessarily required correction before subjection to a desensitization program. The same applies to patients with mistaken attitudes to society, to particular people, or to themselves.

In a 40-year-old woman with multiple neurotic fears, no therapeutic action was possible at first because her anxiety level soared to 80 or 90 suds as soon as she entered the consulting-room. The reason for this was that she had in the course of her adult life come to regard herself as mentally abnormal, mainly due to the attitude of her husband, a physician. This self-conception had, by implication, been reinforced by a psychoanalyst who, over a period of years, had desisted from any statement that might have reassured her. The behavior therapist had to employ every resource of reason and demonstration and the full force of his own prestige to persuade her that she was in truth a normal person who had become disabled by neurotic conditionings acquired in a shockingly severe childhood and extended by an unfortunate marriage. By the sixth session her consulting-room anxiety had fallen to 20 suds, and she had become eagerly co-operative.

Thought Stopping

Certain patients suffer from perseverating and intrusive trains of thought that are unrealistic or unproductive, and also anxiety-arousing in certain cases. One, for example, constantly brooded upon the possibility of a fire breaking out in one of his storehouses although there were no objective fire hazards and he was adequately insured.

The thought-stopping program begins by asking the patient to close his eyes and to verbalize a typical futile thought sequence. During the verbalization the therapist suddenly shouts "Stop!" and then draws attention to the fact that the thoughts actually do stop. This is repeated several times, and the patient is then urged to test the efficacy of the procedure by interrupting his unadaptive *thoughts* by saying "Stop!" subvocally. He is warned that the thoughts will return, and then he is to interrupt them again. In some individuals the main effort is finally directed at learning to stifle each unwanted thought at its inception. The moment it threatens to appear the patient quickly inhibits it by concentrating on something else. The thoughts return less and less readily in many cases and eventually cease to be a problem.

Some years ago, J. W. had an opportunity to test this technique on himself. He had been involved in a legal dispute that was finally settled at a meeting held one morning between the parties and their lawyers. Later that day, reflecting upon the proceedings, he became very disturbed on realizing that he had handled a certain important interchange with singular ineptitude. Dwelling continuously on the matter, he became increasingly distressed. At 7 p.m. the idea occurred to him of putting to the test his own ability to carry out the thought-stopping instructions he so readily offered his patients. This proved to be a very difficult matter, for the thoughts appeared to be borne upon the current of the powerful emotion they aroused. But he strove assiduously, and after about an hour the emotion was noticeably weaker and the thoughts considerably easier to exclude. By 9.30 p.m. he had conquered the problem. The next day, as an experiment, he started to think again of the disturbing incident and very soon the related emotions began to develop. After about 20 minutes of increasing discomfiture he again applied thought-stopping, but it required more than half an hour's "work" to eliminate the "obsession".

Certain modifications of this method are sometimes successful with patients for whom the foregoing standard procedure fails. A fairly uncomfortable faradic shock may be made to accompany the "Stop!" signal and thus disrupt the negative thought-sequence more effectively. Alternatively, the patient may be asked to keep his mind on pleasant thoughts and to press a button which activates a buzzer as soon as any disturbing thoughts intrude. Upon the buzzer sounding the therapist instantly shouts "Stop!" Fifteen minutes per session are usually allowed for this procedure. Frequently, a progressive decline in buzzer-pressing responses is evinced. They may drop from about twenty per minute within the first 2 or 3 min to once every 2 min towards the end of the 15-min period. The patient is then encouraged to practice the exclusion of useless thoughts from his mind on the analogy of this training.

These simple "thought-stopping" techniques sometimes succeed in ameliorating chronic obsessional thinking that has endured for many years. Thought-stopping was introduced by J. G. Taylor in 1955 but was long ago advocated by a largely forgotten writer, James Alexander Bain (1928). Its principle is the building up of the conditioned inhibition of a habit through directly instigated inhibitory behavior. Taylor (1963) has recently described the application of this principle to the treatment of a case of compulsive eyebrow-plucking of 31 years' duration. The habit was overcome in 10 days.

Exaggerated-role Training

In line with Kelly's (1955) fixed-role therapy it has been helpful to instruct some patients deliberately to adopt prescribed roles which are antithetical to their customary behavior. Unlike Kelly, we have not set out to develop major themes, but have confined ourselves to the correction of specific shortcomings, viewing the procedure within the framework of assertive training. A 22-year-old student complained that he always felt extremely awkward and ill at ease when dining at his girl friend's house. On some occasions his mouth had become so dry that he choked over his food. He was instructed more or less as follows:

> The next time you dine at her house I want you to act as if you were a wealthy and important businessman . . . not 22-year-old Peter. As you sit at the table, I want you to look at each person and see him as you think he would appear in the eyes of this mature and wealthy businessman.

In this case the prescribed role, summating, perhaps, with the subsequent eating responses, served to inhibit the patient's anxieties. After one performance of this exaggerated role he experienced no further anxieties in that situation.

Another example relates to a 40-year-old man who became acutely anxious in barber shops. "The worst part is when they have finished your haircut and hold up those little mirrors at the back of your head. I always feel so stupid nodding my head and saying 'Thank you.' . . . I want to rush out of the place. It takes me hours to recover." Exaggerated roletaking was suggested:

> The next time you go to a barber shop I want you to imagine that you are a film star playing the part of a confident and meticulous gentleman having a haircut. The cameras start shooting as you enter the shop and you have to act the part brilliantly so as to please the producer. You must give the barber definite instructions. (*After deliberation.*) These are your lines: "Just trim the back and sides, please . . . I don't want the shorn-sheep look . . . and please take some off the top while you are at it." You must keep pretending that you are not Alan C. . . . but an actor who is very self-assured and relaxed. When he brings you the mirror, you follow the film script and you examine

the result very carefully. You then say: "Would you mind taking just a shade more off the top, please?" Remember to articulate the lines clearly and definitely.

At the next interview the patient reported as follows: "I didn't get an Oscar and actually messed up the ending . . . I couldn't get myself to say the bit about taking more off the top . . . but for the first time I can remember I actually enjoyed myself in the barber's chair."

The Use of Hypnosis

Hypnosis, regarded here as trance behavior based on *verbal conditioning*, may be employed in its own right (direct suggestion, posthypnotic suggestion, training in autohypnosis, the use of time distortion, etc.) or as a therapeutic adjunct, e.g. in systematic desensitization so as to enable certain patients to achieve more vivid and realistic images, and/or deeper and more satisfactory levels of relaxation. It is desirable for the behavior therapist to be proficient at several hypnotic induction techniques and to be well informed about the established phenomena of hypnosis. Excellent coverage of methods and manifestations is provided by Weitzenhoffer (1957). For a systematically objective approach to the problems of the field Hull's classic treatise (1933) is still without peer. The reader is also recommended to the numerous papers of Barber (e.g. 1960, 1962, 1962a, 1964) for their critical appraisal and experimental onslaught on many traditional beliefs about hypnosis.

Intensive Neurotic Response Evocation

Under this heading are subsumed techniques that aim to eliminate neurotic *motor* responses by their repeated unreinforced evocation, and those that attack disturbing emotional habits by intense and prolonged evocation of the emotional response. While the mechanism of the former is clearly the same process of experimental extinction that operates in the removal of all manner of everyday motor habits, the mechanism of the latter is obscure. It seems unlikely to be extinction, if only because in experimentally neurotic animals very prolonged and intense arousal of the emotional reactions does not diminish them (Masserman, 1943; Wolpe, 1952; Appel, 1961). Furthermore, it is often found clinically that the intensity of very strong anxiety reactions tends to be augmented each time they are evoked—an observation confirmed in a human experiment reported by Campbell, Sanderson and Laverty (1964).

Experimental Extinction of Motor Habits

In 1932, Dunlap described the breaking of such habits as typing errors, tics and stammering by persuading the subject to repeat the undesired act again and again, and gave his method the name "negative practice". The method has more recently been mainly used in the treatment of tics (e.g. Yates, 1958; Jones, 1960; Rafi, 1962; Walton, 1964). In thus treating disabling habits by massed practice one has to ensure that the undesirable response is repeated to the point of exhaustion so that a high degree of reactive inhibition is produced. Otherwise the tic may actually be reinforced, especially if the response concerned is not asymptotic to commence with. A severe and chronic case of bruxism in a 26-year-old female was successfully eliminated by massed practice. The patient was instructed to grind her teeth non-stop for 1 min, then to rest for 1 min and to repeat this procedure five times per trial. Each day for approximately 2½ weeks she was required to undergo six trials. At the end of this period her husband reported that involuntary gnashing of her teeth (which had mainly occurred while she was asleep) was no longer present. At a follow-up of almost a year, improvement had been maintained.

Emotional "Flooding" Techniques

In certain patients exposure to intensely anxiety-arousing stimuli has therapeutic results. A technique based on this principle was described by Malleson (1959). It consists of the repeated presentation of strongly anxiety-eliciting imaginary stimuli until the anxiety-evocation is apparently extinguished. One of us (J. W.) tried this method on several patients, and obtained striking success in only one, who had previously benefited in another context from abreactions of the classical kind. He was a dentist who had had an extraordinarily severe and widespread neurosis that had responded markedly to varied and prolonged applications of the usual behavior therapy methods. But there were two residual reactions, of which the more important was an inability to give dental injections because of the horrifying possibility that a patient might die on the chair. As attempts to desensitize him to this were making painfully slow progress, it was decided to try the effects of maximally disturbing stimulation. After the induction of a light hypnotic state he was made to imagine that he had just given a patient an injection, that the patient slumped forward on the chair, and was dead. The dentist became profoundly disturbed, sweated, wept, and wrung his hands. After a minute or so the scene was terminated and a little later re-presented. The reaction reappeared, but weaker. The sequence was further repeated, and by the fifth presentation no reaction whatsoever was observed; he was exhausted, but at ease. The other residuum of the neurosis was similarly treated; and after five more sessions therapy was successfully terminated. Four years later his recovery had been maintained.

A successful case that A. A. L. treated by anxiety-flooding, among other techniques, was Mrs. T., aged 39 years, who had suffered from agoraphobia for nearly 8 years following an episode when she was pregnant and had fainted in the street. She refused to venture out of her house without her husband or her mother. In addition, she had developed an obsessive-compulsive ritual "to repeat the seven times table seven times" whenever the number "seven" was mentioned. Two psychiatrists had previously failed to alleviate her suffering by the application of electroconvulsive therapy, tranquilizers, sedatives, stimulants, sodium pentothal abreactions, relaxation exercises and "insight therapy".

Behavior therapy commenced with desensitization *in vivo* (see p. 141) but slow progress called a halt to this technique. After sixteen sessions she was able to walk only as far as her front gate and refused even to step outside. Attempts at symbolic desensitization were thwarted by repeated anxiety signalling. Inhalations of carbon dioxide and oxygen (see Chapter 7) had "a calming effect" which lasted for several hours. But efforts to base desensitization on carbon dioxide inhalations also proved ineffective. Application of the "anxiety-relief" conditioning method (see below) only generated anxiety, and when the therapist unthinkingly said, "Well, that was the seventh trial," the patient was beset by her obsessional ritual. Several other behavioral techniques including assertive training, differential relaxation, thought-stopping, hypnosis, emotive imagery and environmental manipulation (consisting of instructions to the patient's husband and mother not to reinforce her dependent behavior) all failed to produce any appreciable change.

The first flooding procedure was introduced by the therapist saying the word "seven" into a tape recorder at approximately 10-sec intervals for 1 hr. At subsequent sessions, the tape recorder was switched on for the hour, after which inhalations of carbon dioxide were administered. After the *seventh* session the patient reported that her obsessional ritual was "cured".

In treating the agoraphobia, the most distressing item of her hierarchy—fainting in the street when alone among strangers far from her home—was vividly presented again and again. The therapist delivered a continuous commentary for about 30 min, painting the situation in great detail—the astonished and horrified looks on the faces of passers-by; Mrs. T. being carried into a nearby shop (or being left lying in the street as some people stepped over her while others almost stepped on her); her regaining consciousness from time to time only to faint again; staggering to her feet and then collapsing onto the ground while startled children cried and strange women screamed; lying in the gutter with her thighs exposed while male passers-by had sexual thoughts and reactions.

She responded to these imagined attacks on her dignity in two ways—evincing autonomic reactions, especially blanching, trembling and dyspnoea, and becoming verbally aggressive towards the therapist, calling him sadistic, perverted and cruel. At one stage she threatened to block her ears and run out of the room. This tendency was offset when the therapist momentarily interrupted the flooding sequence to say, "Please observe that no *real* harm comes to you; there is no *real* danger at any time; no one is stabbing you, raping you or beating you." The grueling narrative was then resumed. Approximately 10 min later the patient grew strangely quiet, as though a state of protective inhibition had supervened. She then burst into hysterical laughter which subsided after a few minutes. "This whole thing is so damned absurd," she remarked. Several full-capacity inhalations of pure carbon dioxide were then administered.

Mrs. T. telephoned before her next appointment to inform the therapist that she would only return for further therapy on the understanding that flooding techniques would never again be employed. The therapist agreed, and thereafter employed only desensitization *in vivo* to which she now responded very well. Therapy was then terminated after less than a dozen sessions. More than a year later she was still fully mobile (even to the extent of driving 400 miles on her own to expedite a business transaction for her husband) and no longer suffered from obsessive–compulsive responses. As reported by her husband, she was "infinitely more confident in general".

Real life exposure to situations that are highly disturbing was long ago described by Guthrie (1935), who gave as an example the case of a girl whose car phobia was overcome by her being driven for hours through the streets of Washington, her anxiety in the course of the treatment having reached a great peak. Similar treatment has been employed by existentialist psychotherapists (e.g. Frankl, 1960) under the name *paradoxical intention*, and they have reported many successes with it. The work of Stampfl (as described by London, 1964) carries this "sink-or-swim" principle to its ultimate conclusion.

> He uses every possible means to frighten patients as much as he can for as long as he can at a sitting, taking care only to avoid hurting them physically in any way. He accomplishes this end by the general means of persuading them to imagine themselves realistically involved in situations he describes—and he describes, in copious detail, and with compelling urgency, the most thorough-going catalogue of horrors imaginable; perhaps as rich a collection of lore as was ever composed and narrated for the singular purpose of evoking nauseous terror from even the bravest of men.

Stampfl terminates treatment as soon as it ceases to be possible to elicit anxiety within the session. His fundamental notion in flooding people with anxiety is that when bombarded by fearful cues in a nonreinforcement setting (i.e. when no real harm ensues) extinction will finally supervene.

Because we have seen several cases made much worse by exposure to situations that provoke great anxiety, either in imagination or in reality, we are reluctant to use or recommend the above methods except as a last resort. It would be a different matter if there were ways of predicting when they were likely to be successful, for then much therapeutic time could undoubtedly be saved in the right cases. Without a predictive instrument, however, the greatest caution should be exercised. It is an indispensable preliminary to the routine clinical use of such methods to try out the effects of exposure under varying conditions to stimuli-evoking high-intensity anxiety in neurotic animals. Present experimental evidence (p. 136) includes no instance of deconditioning an animal neurosis through high-intensity stimulation. It is likely that whenever such deconditioning occurs it depends on transmarginal (protective) inhibition—the diminution of response that is observed when stimulus intensity exceeds a certain limit (Pavlov, 1927, 1941; Gray, 1964).

Variants of Systematic Desensitization

Some commonplace parallels of systematic desensitization were mentioned at the beginning of Chapter 5. Consideration will now be given to other clinical methods that follow the desensitization paradigm.

In Vivo *Desensitization*

In contrast with the standard technique, this involves exposing the patient to *real stimuli*. The therapist usually relies on interpersonal and other life circumstances to provide the emotional responses to inhibit anxiety, but relaxation can also be deliberately used, as exemplified by the case of contamination phobia cited in Chapter 5. Successful use of graduated exposures to real stimuli in an institutional setting was reported some years ago by Terhune (1949), working empirically and without awareness of the learning principles involved. The first account of *in vivo* therapy directly based on the desensitization paradigm dealt with two agoraphobic cases treated by Meyer (1957). It was followed in 1960 by Freeman and Kendrick's report of a woman's cat phobia which was overcome by getting her to handle pieces of material which progressively became more and more similar to cat fur, exposing her to pictures of cats, then a toy kitten, followed by a real kitten, and eventually grown cats. A phobia for earthworms has recently been treated in a similar way by Murphy (1964).

In the past few years Meyer has been pursuing this line of work extensively, and in 1963 reported on a group of four diversified cases of social anxiety in whom the most disabling symptom was tremor of the hands while manipulating cutlery, teacups or sherry glasses. One patient's life had become so constricted by the severity of this reaction that at first she appeared to be an agoraphobic. Meyer's technique begins with patient and therapist repeatedly raising an empty glass which is then made progressively fuller, stage by stage, until all signs of shaking disappear; and the same sequence is later repeated before an audience which slowly increases in size. Since no set attempt is made at relaxation, it is inferred that the anxiety is inhibited by emotions aroused in the patient by his interaction with the therapist. All four of these patients were treated in hospital, and recovered after a few weeks of intensive therapy.

We frequently have recourse to *in vivo* methods, usually not out of choice but when it is not feasible to make use of imagined or symbolic stimuli. Treatment may then take the form of directed, graded exposures to real situations as exemplified by Meyer's cases above, and we have treated cases of agoraphobia by graduated separations of the patient from ourselves in the field—literally! Sometimes we abstract the essential aspect of disturbing situations and devise "office" equivalents to expose the patient to controlled "doses" of neurotic anxiety. For example, in a case of fear of public speaking based on fear of humiliation the therapist first made the patient deliberately give wrong answers to simple arithmetical problems, went on to more difficult problems (some of which the patient really failed) and then had him stumble in his own field (constitutional law). At each stage the patient was derided for his "errors". Witnesses were later introduced to watch the sequence of failures.

Group Desensitization

This is really desensitization in the orthodox manner, performed in a group setting, and was first described by Lazarus (1960, 1961). Several individuals with the same kind of phobia, e.g. acrophobia, were treated simultaneously, the therapist taking an upward step in the hierarchy only when every patient in the group could endure the previous step without anxiety. About two-thirds of these patients recovered in a mean of 20·4 desensitization sessions, giving a mean session expenditure of about 3·5 per patient. In large psychiatric units there may be many patients with the same phobia, and group desensitization could obviously then effect great savings of therapist time. But it is important to realize that this method is no panacea, and cannot be the sole therapeutic agent except when a patient's disturbance is limited to a particular phobia.

Emotive Imagery

The use of anxiety-inhibiting emotive images (i.e. images that arouse feelings of pride, mirth, the excitement of adventure, serenity, or affection) has been shown to be highly effective in treating phobic children (Lazarus and Abramovitz, 1962). The technique consists of the following steps:

(a) As in the usual method of systematic desensitization, a graduated hierarchy is drawn up.
(b) By sympathetic conversation and inquiry, the clinician establishes the nature of the child's hero images and the wish fulfilments and identifications which accompany them.
(c) The child is asked to close his eyes and imagine a sequence of events which is close enough to his everyday life to be credible, but within which is woven a story concerning his favorite hero or *alter ego*.
(d) When the clinician judges that these emotions have been maximally aroused, he introduces, as a natural part of the narrative, the lowest item in the hierarchy. If there is evidence that anxiety is being inhibited, the procedure is repeated as in ordinary systematic desensitization until the highest item in the hierarchy is tolerated without distress.

The following illustrative case is taken from Lazarus and Abramovitz (1962):

Stanley M., aged 14, suffered from an intense fear of dogs which had lasted for 2½–3 years. He would take two buses on a roundabout route to school rather than risk exposure to dogs on a direct 300-yard walk. He was a rather dull (I.Q. 93), sluggish person, very large for his age, trying to be co-operative, but sadly unresponsive—especially to attempts at training in relaxation. In his desire to please, he would state that he had been perfectly relaxed even though he had betrayed himself by his intense fidgetiness. Training in relaxation was eventually abandoned, and an attempt was made to establish the nature of his aspirations and goals. By dint of much questioning and after following many false trails because of his inarticulateness, a topic was eventually tracked down that was absorbing enough to form the subject of his fantasies, namely racing motor-cars. He had a burning ambition to own a certain Alfa-Romeo sports car and race it at the Indianapolis "500" event. Emotive imagery was induced as follows: "Close your eyes. I want you to imagine, clearly and vividly, that your wish has come true. The Alfa-Romeo is now in your possession. It is your car. It is standing in the street outside your house. You are looking at it now. Notice the beautiful, sleek lines. You decide to go for a drive with some friends of yours. You sit down at the wheel, and you feel a thrill of pride as you realize that you own this magnificent machine. You start up and listen to the wonderful roar of the exhaust. You let the clutch in and the car streaks off. You are out in a clear open road now; the speedometer is climbing into the nineties; you have a wonderful feeling of being in perfect control; you look at the trees whizzing by and you see a little dog standing next to one of them—if you feel any anxiety, just raise your finger. Etc., etc." An item fairly high up on the hierarchy was: "You stop at a café in a little town, and dozens of people crowd around to look enviously at this magnificent car and its lucky owner; you swell with pride; and at this moment a large boxer comes up and sniffs at your heels. If you feel any anxiety, etc., etc."

After three sessions with this method he reported a marked improvement in his reaction to dogs. He was given a few field assignments during the next two sessions, after which therapy was terminated. Twelve months later, reports received from both the patient and his relatives indicated that there was no longer any trace of his former phobia.

The recent use of this technique with adults has been most promising. A patient who reports distinct anxiety diminution when imagining himself in front of a glowing log fire on a winter's evening may profit more readily from a desensitization program which relies on images of this kind than he would from desensitization based on relaxation. Relaxation and emotive imagery may also be used in combination. It is often very helpful for a patient to relax and picture a pleasant subjective scene during the interval between the presentation of desensitization items. Also the development of anxiety reduction is often helped when noxious stimuli are verbally presented to patients with instructions to picture themselves coping with the situation in a completely relaxed and confident manner: "See yourself calmly rebuking the waitress, feel the confidence and relaxed sensations throughout." Emotive imagery *in vivo* is also of distinct therapeutic value. A competitive swimmer who was overwhelmed by anxiety in between competitive events derived no benefit from hypnosis, anxiety-relief conditioning, desensitization and several other techniques. He was excited but non-anxious at the beginning of each race, but grew extremely anxious during the rest interval between the events, and this undermined his performance. The use of emotive imagery solved his difficulty. He could vividly imagine himself walking along a sandy beach, an image which generated profound feelings of tranquility, and he effectively employed this device when necessary. Soon thereafter he was chosen for the Olympic Games.

Feeding Responses

The mere fact that more than 40 years have passed since Jones (1924) applied the anxiety-inhibiting properties of feeding responses to a clinical problem is no reason for regarding her technique as a matter of historical interest only. By inducing a phobic child to eat in the presence of a feared object (a rabbit in a cage which was very gradually brought nearer the child as he sat eating) she completely eliminated the child's fears. Many present-day clinicians have used eating responses in an operant setting in which tasty snacks, chocolate, etc., were made contingent upon predetermined responses. Lazarus (1960) described the treatment of an anxious child by offering chocolate according to both operant conditioning and respondent conditioning requirements. The child, who was terrified of travelling in moving vehicles, was given chocolate as a reinforcer for the operant behavior of talking about cars, then sitting in cars, and finally for riding in cars. In the same manner, various conditioned stimuli such as toy cars were paired with the unconditioned stimuli of eating chocolate which generated pleasurable responses which, in turn, became conditioned to vehicle stimuli.

It is possible that the voracious hunger drive usually stimulated by subcoma doses of insulin could be put to more effective clinical use if the rules of conditioning were observed. The results previously reported for subcoma insulin treatment with neuroses (e.g. Sargant and Slater, 1947) have been insipid, but this may be due to the failure of the clinician to pair the consequent eating behavior deliberately and systematically with anxiety-producing stimuli. A passive reliance on the fortuitous occurrence of anxiety-generating stimuli at the time of eating is not likely to help patients, except perhaps those suffering from pervasive anxiety, and then only temporarily (see p. 124).

Desensitization Based on Inhibition of Anxiety by a Conditioned Motor Response

This technique, though first reported more than a decade ago (Wolpe, 1954), has so far been very little used. It was suggested by an observation of Mowrer and Viek (1948) that when animals are enabled to learn a definite motor response to electrical stimulation they gradually develop conditioned inhibition of the autonomic responses that are evoked at the same time on repetition of the stimulation. For this procedure, the electrodes of an inductorium are attached to the patient's nondominant hand and forearm. The patient is then instructed to close his eyes and to imagine a disturbing situation (usually selected from an anxiety hierarchy in the conventional way). A prearranged signal informs the therapist when the image is vivid and realistic, whereupon a *mild* faradic shock is delivered, being stopped only on the occurrence of a brisk flexion of the forearm into which the current is being passed (the patient having been instructed beforehand to carry out this flexion of his arm upon receiving the shock). In an extreme case of agoraphobia (whose completely successful treatment has been described in detail by Wolpe (1958)) it was found that, as a rule, fifteen to twenty-five flexions were needed to bring down to zero the anxiety response to a disturbing scene.

Lazarus (1965) has reported another method of procuring the reciprocal inhibition of anxiety by the use of motor responses. The patient is instructed to perform forceful muscular activity (e.g. a rapid volley of blows at a suspended punch-bag, or strenuous slamming of palms and forearms onto a sturdy and well-upholstered bedstead) *in immediate association with an anxiety-provoking, or otherwise disturbing, thought or image.* In some cases, this has been found to ameliorate anxious and depressive reactions progressively.

Desensitization Based on Galvanic Shock Interference

Two distinct techniques have lately been introduced, both of which seem quite promising, while still experimental. They were brought to our attention by Dr. William M. Philpott of Takoma Park, Maryland, who had noted the efficacy of galvanic stimuli while seeking ways of procuring desensitization without using muscle relaxation.

(a) *Mild galvanic stimulation.* Our present technique, which has been modified from Dr. Philpott's as the result of controlled experiments performed at the University of Virginia, is as follows. Attached to the patient's wrist and below his elbow are wet electrodes consisting of saline-soaked strips of gauze held in place by alligator clips connected to the apparatus. Galvanic pulses are delivered from a dry 90-volt battery by pressing a push-button, the on–off cycle taking about a second. The current is controlled by a variable resistance, and the "correct" current for the patient, established by trial and error, is at a level which is strongly felt *without being aversive.* We used to accompany each pulse with the word "relax" but it is now almost certain that this makes little or no difference. If the patient has pervasive anxiety, 8–10 pulses per minute gradually reduce the anxiety, and in 20–30 min it is usually brought very low—sometimes down to zero. These effects may be due to Pavlov's *external inhibition.*

When pervasive anxiety is at a low level the therapist presents scenes to the patient from his anxiety hierarchies, administering a pulse (with or without the word "relax") two or three times during the scene. Decrements of anxiety response occur as with conventional desensitization but require more presentations.

(b) *Strong galvanic stimulation.* In some patients the intrusion of mild galvanic stimulation on the anxiety evoked by hierarchical stimuli does not produce any decrease in the level of anxiety. It is a remarkable fact that in certain of these cases the anxiety level is reduced when the galvanic stimulation is made strong enough to evoke vigorous contraction of the forearm muscles.

In other individuals such strong electrical stimuli would only produce mounting anxiety.

The following is the technique that we employ at present. Wet electrodes are applied to the patient's right forearm in the same way as when mild shock is used. The fearful situation is presented *alone* once or twice to the patient in imagination in order to determine the level of anxiety (in suds) that it produces. The variable resistance is then set at a reading at which the galvanic stimulus has previously been found adequate by trial and error to produce a strong muscle contraction. The patient is asked to imagine the scene at issue, and to signal by raising his left index finger when the scene is well defined. Upon this, the therapist administers two galvanic shocks separated by about a second. After about 5 sec the patient is instructed to re-form the scene, signaling as before when this has been accomplished. After a series of five to ten scenes with shock the status of the reaction to the scene is determined by presenting it without any shock.

An early case of J. W.'s to be treated by this method was a woman whose many-faceted neurosis had been largely overcome by the usual behavior therapy methods. One troublesome neurotic constellation that remained was a phobia for driving alone. Originally she could not drive her car up her own driveway without feeling anxious. She had progressed steadily but slowly with ordinary desensitization until she was able to drive her car for three-quarters of a mile without any discomfort. One day, a disturbing incident occurred at a place half a mile from home, and she was thereafter unable to go beyond this point. Rather than resume the desensitization that had proved so tedious in her case, it was resolved to try galvanic stimulation. Mild stimulation was completely ineffective; but the use of the strong stimulus while she visualized herself at that critical place half a mile from home at once yielded decrements of anxiety. After twenty shocks anxiety had decreased to zero. When she later tested herself in life she found that she was completely free from anxiety at the three-quarter-mile point. By this method the patient subsequently made much swifter progress than had ever been possible with ordinary desensitization.

Conditioning of "Anxiety-relief" Responses

If an unpleasant stimulus is endured for several seconds and is then made to cease almost immediately after a specified signal, that signal may become conditioned to the changes that follow cessation of the uncomfortable stimulus. The patient experiences these changes as a feeling of "relief". Thus, if he endures an uncomfortable induction shock and says aloud the word "calm" when he strongly desires the shock to stop, and if the termination of the shock produces this feeling of relief this may become conditioned to the word "calm" by repetition. "Anxiety-relief" conditioning occurs in those patients who experience some degree of *emotional* disturbance (as opposed to mere sensory discomfort) in response to the electric shocks. The feeling of relief may be quite profound and out of proportion to the disturbing effect of the shock. The administration of drugs that augment sympathetic responses (e.g. amphetamines) apparently facilitates the conditioning. By uttering the word "calm" in disturbing life situations, successfully conditioned subjects may experience an immediate decrease of anxiety, and this may be used to build up conditioned inhibition of anxiety in the situations concerned. But even when conditioned inhibition is not effected, the anxiety-relief conditioning in itself gives many patients worthwhile relief from individual attacks of anxiety.

There are several ways in which "anxiety relief" may be conditioned, the three most usual being: (a) steady-shock escape; (b) increasing-shock escape; and (c) shock avoidance.

(a) *Steady-shock escape.* The electrodes leading from a faradic unit (the secondary circuit of an induction coil) are attached by means of rubber bands to the forearm and palm of the patient's nondominant hand. Tests are then conducted to establish a level of shock that is distinctly uncomfortable but not unbearable. Shock of this intensity is then administered continuously, the patient having been told beforehand to endure the discomfort until the desire for relief from shock becomes very strong, and then to say aloud the word "calm". Immediately after the word is said, the current is switched off. After a 30–60-sec rest pause the procedure is repeated. This is done ten to twenty times at a session. In order to avoid the build-up of anxiety between shocks, patients must be informed that they will never be shocked without warning.

(b) *Increasing-shock escape.* Instead of administering the shock at a steady high intensity, the level of shock delivered is low at first and then increased so that in 5–10 sec it is powerful enough for the patient to feel a strong need to have it stopped. He then says the word "calm", upon which the therapist terminates the shock. It is important to increase the shock gradually and steadily. Patients may be urged to withstand higher and higher intensities of shock before saying "calm" to bring about greater measures of relief at its cessation.

(c) *Shock avoidance.* With the foregoing shock-escape procedures, many individuals merely experience relief from *sensory* discomfort, since the shock induces little or no anxiety in them and anxiety-relief conditioning is not established. Some of them respond to the following technique.

A powerful current is delivered until the patient says "calm" (usually instantaneously). A second and more powerful current is administered 30 seconds later. The patient is then informed that the therapist will say the word "shock" and that a still more powerful current will be switched on about 10 sec later. The patient is told to anticipate the shock for at least 5 sec and then to say the word "calm" if he wishes to avoid the shock. Most patients display definite signs of tension and anxiety during the waiting interval. As soon as they say the word "calm" (thus avoiding the shock) many of them feel marked anxiety relief. It is quite usual to find that the word "calm" becomes an effective anxiety-reducing stimulus in the life situation after as few as thirty trials. (A case treated by this method is mentioned on p. 21.)

The effects of the techniques outlined above are often enhanced when the patient deliberately relaxes immediately after saying the stimulus word. The word "calm" then becomes associated with shock cessation or shock avoidance *plus* the pleasurable feelings of muscle relaxation.

Aversive Conditioning

The treatment of alcoholism by developing a revulsion towards alcohol through the deliberate induction of nausea and vomiting by emetine or apomorphine has been going on for a quarter of a century (e.g. Lemere and Voegtlin, 1950). Kantorovich (1929) used painful electric shocks for the same purpose. The same agents have also been employed to procure aversion towards obsessionally attractive objects or ideas. Max (1935), using faradic shocks to overcome a homosexual fetish, was the first to employ them in this way. In recent years aversion therapy has been applied to the treatment of obsessional ruminations and compulsive eating (e.g. Wolpe, 1958, p. 183), fetishism (Raymond, 1956), homosexuality (Freund, 1960; James, 1962), transvestism (Glynn and Harper, 1961; Blakemore, 1965) as well as to the addictions: alcoholism, narcotic addiction and smoking (McGuire and Vallance, 1964).

Faradic shock is the preferred agent because it affords much more accurate time relations. Depending upon the circumstances of the case, one may administer the shock either in relation to the actual objects or situations that form the basis of the obsessional behavior, or ask the patient to imagine the object or situation. The standard procedure is to attach the electrodes to the patient's left forearm. The setting of the inductorium is determined by gradually increasing the shock to a point where the patient reports that it is distinctly unpleasant. The starting point for avoidance conditioning is then approximately 0·5 cm beyond (i.e. more unpleasant than the point indicated). When real stimuli are used the shock is terminated as soon as the avoidance responses are made, e.g. as soon as the alcoholic turns away from the brandy. Those who are *imagining* situations are told to indicate by means of a prearranged signal as soon as the shock becomes unbearable, and then it is terminated.

Best results are obtained when the conditioning program is conducted on at least a daily basis to the point of "overlearning". At least twenty CS-UCS pairings are recommended per session. Severe cases may require three or more sessions each day.

Recent reports (e.g. Thorpe *et al.*, 1964; Feldman and MacCulloch, 1965) have demonstrated the value of combining aversion therapy with anxiety-relief conditioning. In treating homosexuality the patient is given a painful shock in the presence of a homosexual image on a screen and then a heterosexual picture is flashed onto the screen in temporal contiguity with the cessation of the shock. Homosexual associations thus become anxiety-generating (and result in *avoidance* responses), whereas heterosexual stimuli become conditioned to anxiety relief (and acquire *approach* valences).

We regard it as poor practice to embark on aversive therapy without first ascertaining if the obsessional behavior is a consequence of anxiety, which must then be treated first. Failure to observe this rule may lead to "symptom substitution" (Lazarus, 1965). On the other hand, after deconditioning the emotional habit, it frequently turns out that it is unnecessary to do anything about the obsessional behavior as such. The proper indications for aversion therapy are found when the obsessional behavior is either unrelated to anxiety *ab initio* or is found to persist autonomously after anxiety has been deconditioned.

Recently, a portable faradic shock apparatus (McGuire and Vallance, 1964) has shown interesting potentialities. It seems likely that an important reason for the limited success of aversion treatment of alcoholism is that it has been customary to apply it only in connection with the sight, smell and taste of the drug. No attempt is ordinarily made to combat the feelings of craving that arise endogenously, partly because of the impossibility of producing the craving at will in the consulting-room. The difficulty is overcome by the portable faradic shock apparatus. A physician with a demerol (pethidine) addiction of 4 years' standing was instructed to give himself a severe shock whenever he felt a desire for the drug. On three occasions he gave himself four, three and two severe shocks respectively. After this the apparatus broke down, but the patient felt only minor cravings that he could easily control for a period of 12 weeks (Wolpe, 1965). It is felt that this single experiment is striking enough to justify more extensive trials by psychiatrists who have to contend with problems of drug addiction. (Also see Lazarus, 1965b for an account of "broad-spectrum behavior therapy" in the treatment of alcoholism.)

CHAPTER 9

The Results of Behavior Therapy

THE late Alexander Kennedy once said that psychotherapy is not a sport. There can be only one justification for advocating that behavior therapy should displace the present psychoanalytically based systems of psychotherapy, and that is the conviction that it is substantially more efficacious in overcoming neurotic disturbances. Practitioners very easily acquire a belief in the efficacy of their chosen psychotherapeutic system because, as has repeatedly been shown (e.g. Landis, 1937; Wilder, 1945; Eysenck, 1952), 40 or 50 per cent of neurotic patients improve markedly with conventional therapies despite widely differing theories and practices. It is difficult to escape the inference that the beneficial effects obtained are not derived from procedures special to any of these therapies, but emerge from some process that is common to all of them—presumably the emotional impact on the patient of the therapist, a trusted and supposedly wise and competent person to whom he unburdens himself. Therapists who are aware of these nonspecific therapeutic effects are not entitled to claim special virtues for their particular practices, unless they obtain either a percentage of recoveries substantially above the common average, or greater rapidity of recovery.

It is because there are factual grounds for believing that behavior therapy exceeds the common average in *both* the percentage and speed of recovery that its techniques are confidently offered in this volume. This confidence necessarily falls short of that which would result from impeccably controlled and repeated clinical trials. But it is a considerable confidence, based partly on impressive, though uncontrolled, clinical experience, and partly on a few very well controlled experimental studies.

These are presented below. Some studies purporting to challenge the claims of behavior therapy are also examined.

Uncontrolled Clinical Studies

An increasing number of reports of individual cases or small groups treated by behavior therapy have been appearing during the past decade. Many of these reports have been conveniently brought together and classified in two volumes edited by Eysenck (1960, 1965); and an annotated list (Wolpe *et al.*, 1964) cites others.

The first statistical study to be published was a survey by Wolpe (1958) of his results of 9 years of private practice of behavior therapy. Almost 90 per cent of his 210 patients were rated as either apparently cured or much improved in a mean of about thirty therapeutic sessions. Every case diagnosed as neurotic was accepted for treatment if therapeutic time was available. Psychotics and psychopaths were not knowingly accepted, and, if treated through error of diagnosis, transferred to other therapists when the mistake was discovered. In a group of eighteen phobic children treated by Lazarus (1960) all recovered in a mean of 9·5 sessions. Recently, Lazarus (1963) reviewed the results of his private practice, and found that of 408 patients who had consulted him, 321 (78 per cent) had derived marked benefit on very stringent criteria. It should be noted that Lazarus included in his series *all* his neurotic patients—even those whom he had seen only once. This, of course, gives a negative bias to the recovery rate. Cases to whom behavior therapy techniques were never applied do not properly belong in a behavior therapy evaluation. In a more recent appraisement of his results Lazarus found a recovery rate of 86 per cent in those cases with whom behavior therapy had been given "a fair trial".

Table 5 (p. 162) places the results of the foregoing studies in juxtaposition with those of a typical series from a general hospital, and two psychoanalytical series. A substantially higher percentage of recoveries is shown for behavior therapy; but since the various series are not matched the comparison may be distorting the truth. However, a controlled comparison would not necessarily be less favorable to behavior therapy. Whatever the correct *percentages* may turn out to be, the comparison of sessions spent in therapy is overwhelmingly in favor of behavior therapy. The mean number of sessions for psychoanalysis is in the region 600—3 or 4 times a week for 3 or 4 years (Masserman, 1963); while the mean for behavior therapy is about 30. The practical implications of this contrast seem inescapable.

There are three other published reports that present uncontrolled statistical data on the results of behavior therapy. The findings of the first two are in line with our own, and the third is to some extent discordant, but these reports really do not have much evaluative relevance to the battery of techniques described in this book—for reasons that we shall give. Hussain (1964) has claimed a 95 per cent "complete or almost complete removal of symptoms" in 105 patients whose disturbed habits were treated by hypnotic suggestions based on the reciprocal inhibition principle; but the details of his method are not very clear, and the criteria of change are not reported in detail. Burnett and Ryan (1964) treated 100 patients by giving them relaxation training, and desensitization to both imaginary and real situations, in groups, and sometimes individually. Treatment continued for 5 weeks on the average. A 1-year follow-up could only be carried out on 25 of the patients, of whom 15 (60 per cent) were found to be either apparently cured or much improved. The brief exposure of the patients to behavior therapy and the predominance of group procedures tend to bias the outcome negatively (see Lazarus, 1961) because they do not permit a full exploitation of the resources available. Nevertheless, the 60 per cent recovery rate after such brief therapy seems quite noteworthy; and the authors were much encouraged by their findings.

A writer who, in contrast with those cited above, finds that his improvement rate with behavior therapy "contrasts very unfavorably with Wolpe's" is McConaghy (1964). In summary, his treatment of eighteen patients yielded four with marked improvement and five with moderate improvement. However, there are several reasons for regarding any comparison as inadmissible. Fifteen of the eighteen cases had failed to respond to, or were considered unsuitable for, conventional psychiatric treatment; at least three were psychotic; avoidance therapy was used in no less than six of the remaining patients without first attempting to decondition the underlying emotional reactions; and when treatment was instituted on the desensitization model it was always *in vivo*—where it is hard to ensure control of inhibition of anxiety. Finally, it is not evident that McConaghy performed adequate stimulus-response analyses in most of his cases.

The opinion is frequently expressed that the effects of behavior therapy are "superficial" because it does not remove the basic neurosis, and that relapse and symptom substitution are to be expected. This opinion, of course, presupposes the truth of the psychoanalytical view of the nature of neurosis—and there are many reasons for doubting that view (Wohlgemuth, 1923; Salter, 1952; Eysenck, 1952, 1953, 1965; Wolpe and Rachman, 1960; Wolpe, 1961; Rachman, 1963). Behavior therapists rarely encounter anything like relapse and when they do it is usually quite clear that there has been *reconditioning*. Wolpe (1958) had only one relapse among forty-five patients followed-up from 2 to 7 years. Symptom substitution is apparently only found when therapy is carried out without attention to the autonomic core of neurotic reactions (see, for example, some of McConaghy's cases referred to above and Lazarus's (1965) discussion of complete and incomplete behavior therapy).

Another question frequently raised is whether behavior therapy is able to effect "personality change". If personality is defined as a person's totality of habits of behavior, it is obvious that the elimination of neurotic habits is in itself a kind of personality change. When a patient is relieved of his neurotic disturbance he is also rendered progressively freer to behave effectively in various sectors of life. Motor habits are often automatically changed when the patient is freed from the restrictions imposed by neurotic anxiety. Other habits may be deliberately reshaped. If personality change is conceived in terms of habit change, it at once becames possible to compare psychoanalysis with behavior therapy as a means of producing a stated category of change. As yet such comparisons have not been made and until they are made there will be no basis for the assertion that psychoanalysis is a "better" agent for producing "fundamental personality change".

Controlled Studies of Outcome

There have to date been three controlled outcome studies, each dealing with systematic desensitization. The first of these, by Lazarus (1961), compared the results of treating phobias, such as claustrophobia (fear of enclosed spaces) and acrophobia (fear of heights), by two different forms of group therapy. The patients were separated into matched pairs, and then by the toss of a coin one member of a pair was placed in a desensitization group and the other in a conventional "dynamic" group. After twenty-one sessions, 72 per cent of the patients in the desensitization groups had recovered, as compared with a 12 per cent recovery rate in the "dynamic" groups (see Table 6, p. 163).

At the University of Illinois, Gordon L. Paul (1966) performed a very elaborate study comparing desensitization with two other methods in members of a public speaking class who had severe fears of speaking in public. He enlisted and paid for the services of five experienced psychotherapists whose "school" affiliation ranged from Freud to Sullivan. Nine cases were allotted to each therapist, who was required to use three different methods—each in three subjects. The methods were: (1) the therapist's own customary type of insight therapy; (2) a stylized procedure involving suggestion and support called "attention-placebo" therapy; and (3) systematic desensitization (in which the therapists had to be trained beforehand by the experimenter). Each patient received five therapeutic sessions. The results showed significantly superior effectiveness for systematic desensitization on a variety of measures. In terms of conventional clinical change (Table 7), 86 per cent of the patients treated by desensitization were much improved and 14 per cent improved. In the insight group 20 per cent were much improved and 27 per cent improved; and in the attention-placebo group none were much improved and 47 per cent improved.

The third set of controlled investigations is due to Lang and Lazovik (1963) and Lang, Lazovik and Reynolds (1965). Their subjects were students who had severe phobic reactions to harmless snakes. They treated some of them by systematic desensitization, and compared the results with those of two control groups—one that received no treatment and another that received "pseudotherapy" (i.e. relaxation training followed by interviews focusing on problems of "living", with the patient in a state of relaxation). The desensitized students improved very much more than either of the control groups, as shown by a snake avoidance test and by the patient's self-rating of fear reaction to snakes (Table 8). The difference was very significant when fifteen or more hierarchy items were desensitized.

In strong contrast to the above are the *clinical* "controlled studies" of Cooper (1963), Gelder, Marks, Sakinovsky and Wolff (1964) and Gelder and Marks (1965) which purport to compare, in ordinary clinical practice, the results of behavior therapy with those of conventional "dynamic" psychotherapy. These investigators have evidently made up their minds that "anybody can do behavior therapy", and consequently regard the results of anybody who dabbles with it as a yardstick of its efficacy. In their eyes, a person who sets out to apply the principles of behavior therapy is *ipso facto* a behavior therapist; and prominent in their studies are the fledgling efforts of novices who have learned the rudiments of systematic desensitization. For many years, those of us who have been skeptical of the claims of psychoanalysts have pleaded for controlled comparative outcome studies, but we would only have regarded as relevant the work of well-trained, experienced psychoanalysts. Psychoanalysts would justifiably disclaim, as being unrepresentative of their own capability, the work of those not qualified in psychoanalysis. Behavior therapists are likewise entitled to have their craft judged upon the work of the expert and not of the amateur.

Despite their lack of experience, the "behavior therapists" who participated in the investigations of Cooper and of Gelder *et al.* did produce relatively rapid changes in some patients, but the investigators note that the advantage over "psychotherapy" becomes insignificantly small after a year's follow-up. A conclusion appropriate to the facts would appear to be that even crude behavior therapy is sometimes a little better than conventional psychotherapy.

The Criteria of Therapeutic Change

Broadly speaking, the goal of psychotherapy is the same as that of any other branch of therapeutics—the lasting removal of the sources of suffering and disability. If the attainment of that goal were always an all-or-nothing matter, evaluation would be relatively easy; but recoveries are frequently only partial and hence there is a need for some means of measurement.

Since the behavior therapist views the therapeutic task as a matter of eliminating persistent unadaptive *habits*, the most appropriate way of measuring his success would be to classify and enumerate the unadaptive habits before therapy, and then, after therapy, to assess to what extent each habit has been eliminated. In making such assessments the therapist can employ several kinds of information—the report of the patient, clinical observations, the observations of associates of the patient, and psychophysiological studies. The last named are basic and should be a prominent feature of almost every study concerned with results of therapy.

In clinical practice, however, it is appropriate to employ clinical criteria such as those delineated by Knight (1941) as a step towards improving the rigor of psychoanalytical research. Knight's criteria have been explicitly adopted by behavior therapists (but hardly at all by psychoanalysts). They are as follows:

1. Symptomatic improvement.
2. Increased productiveness at work.
3. Improved adjustment and pleasure in sex.

4. Improved interpersonal relationships.
5. Enhanced ability to handle ordinary psychological conflicts and reasonable reality stresses.

Although several of these criteria can be applied to most cases, the only one that is always relevant is "symptomatic improvement", because a neurosis need not interfere with all or any of the specified functions. A man with neurotic anxieties in work situations may have a completely satisfying sex life and be at ease in social situations. If symptomatic improvement is obtained by palliative means such as drugs, this does not qualify as attainment of Knight's first criterion. The criterion requires *fundamental* change in that stimuli that used to call forth inappropriate anxiety or other unadaptive responses no longer can do so *under the same conditions*. In other words, the patient is at ease in situations in which he was formerly disturbed, without the aid of drugs or other crutches.

What the patient perceives as a symptom, the therapist perceives as a habit. By deconditioning the anxiety-response habit that is the basis of the anxiety symptom, we necessarily bring about a commensurate diminution of the symptom. If there have been other reactions that are secondary to the presence of the anxiety, they too diminish or cease—whether they have appeared in the form of migraine, asthma, neurodermatitis, fibrositis, stammering, frigidity, impotence or homosexuality, or grosser behavior such as compulsions or seclusiveness. The decline of each secondary manifestation of neurosis is thus also a measure of improvement.

It is a particular merit of the behavioristic approach that change can be evaluated exclusively in terms of clearly defined referents. This is much more practicable than to be concerned with "repressed complexes", or working through the "Oedipus constellation", or bringing about "recession of childhood transference". We know of no scientifically acceptable evidence of anything of the sort being implicated in the cause or maintenance of neuroses.

There is one major reform that we should like to see in all future outcome studies. Gelder and Marks (1965) have drawn attention to the confusing consequences of the traditional practice of lumping together all kinds of neuroses. Although categorization is not always easy, particularly in cases with widespread neuroses, it would facilitate comparisons, and make it possible to determine to what extent different syndromes may require different measures. It is, in retrospect, rather ludicrous to have been comparing different therapies on the basis of varied assortments of, for example, phobias, tics and homosexuality.

These melanges are an offshoot of psychoanalytic theory, which plays down the outward features of neuroses because it assumes the "real" pathology to be "inside". When neuroses are seen as habits, their subdivisions are different from the psychoanalytic ones. Thus, most character neuroses turn out to be based on neurotic anxiety habits, and reactive depressions are seen as consequents of anxiety that is unusually intense or prolonged.

TABLE 5. UNCONTROLLED OUTCOME STUDIES (see pp. 155–156)

Series	Number of cases	Apparently cured or much improved (recoveries)	Percentage recoveries
Behavior therapy			
Wolpe (1958)	210	188	89·5
Lazarus (1963)	410	321	78·0
Psychoanalytic therapy			
Collected series of psychoneuroses (Knight, 1941)			
(a) Over 6 months' therapy ..	383	242	63·2
(b) Total cases	534		45·3
Pshycoanalytic factfinding committee (Brody, 1962). *Completely analyzed cases only*	210	126	60
General hospital therapy			
New York Hospital (Hamilton and Wall, 1941)	100	53	53

TABLE 6. NUMBER OF PATIENTS ASSIGNED TO EACH CONDITION AND THE THERAPEUTIC OUTCOME

Patients	Treated by desensitization	Recovered	Treated by interpretation	Recovered	Treated by interpretation and relaxation	Recovered
Acrophobics ..	5	4	3	0	0	1
Claustrophobics	7	4	3	0	5	1
Impotence ..	2	2	3	0	—	—
Mixed group ..	4	3	—	—	—	—
Total ..	18	13	9	0	8	2

Lazarus (1961).

TABLE 7. PERCENTAGE BREAKDOWN OF CASES IN TRADITIONAL "IMPROVEMENT" CATEGORIES FROM STRESS CONDITION DATA (see text)

Treatment group	No.	Unimproved %	"Improvement" classification		
			Slightly improved %	Improved %	Much improved %
Desensitization ..	15	—	—	14	86
Insight	15	7	4	27	20
Attention placebo ..	15	20	33	47	—
Treatment control ..	29	55	28	17	—

Gordon L. Paul (1966)

TABLE 8. T-TESTS OF MEAN FEAR CHANGE SCORES FROM PRE- TO POST-TREATMENT

Groups	Avoid-ance test	Fear thermo-meter	FSS No. 38	Fear survey
Combined control *vs.* Desensitization	2·57*	2·12*	2·19*	1·25
Combined control *vs.* 15 or more	3·26†	3·44†	3·99‡	2·52*
Combined control *vs.* Less than 15	0·14	0·41	1·85	0·41
Less than 15 *vs.* 15 or more	2·33*	3·28*	5·00‡	2·26*
Pseudotherapy *vs.* No treatment	1·67	0·48	0·58	0·12

* $p < 0{\cdot}05$. † $p < 0{\cdot}01$. ‡ $p < 0{\cdot}001$.

Lang, Lazovik and Reynolds, *J. Abnorm. Pshycol.* (1965).

APPENDIX 1

Life History Questionnaire

Purpose of this questionnaire

The purpose of this questionnaire is to obtain a comprehensive picture of your background. In scientific work, records are necessary, since they permit a more thorough dealing with one's problems. By completing these questions as fully and as accurately as you can, you will facilitate your therapeutic program. This questionnaire will save you both time and expense. You are requested to answer these routine questions in your own time instead of using up your actual consulting time.

It is understandable that you might be concerned about what happens to the information about you, because much or all of this information is highly personal. Case records are strictly confidential. *No outsider, not even your closest relative or family doctor, is permitted to see your case record without your written permission.*

N.B. If you do not desire to answer any question, merely write "Do not care to answer."

Date:..............................

1. GENERAL

Name: ....

Address: ....

.... Telephone Numbers:....................

Age:.................... ....

Occupation: ....

With whom are you now living? (List people): ....

....

Do you live in a house, hotel, room, apartment, etc.?............................

Marital status: single; engaged; married; re-married; separated; divorced; widowed.

How strongly do you want treatment for your problem? Very much. Much. Moderately. Could do without it if necessary.

2. CLINICAL

State in your own words the nature of your chief complaint: ....

....

Give a brief account of the history and development of your complaint (from onset to present): ....

....

Whom have you previously consulted about your present problem?

....

Underline any of the following that apply to you:

headaches; dizziness; fainting spells; palpitations; stomach trouble; no appetite; bowel disturbances; fatigue; insomnia; nightmares; take sedatives; alcoholism; feel tense; feel panicky; tremors; depressed; suicidal ideas; drugs; unable to relax; sexual problems; unable to have a good time; don't like weekends and vacations; over-ambitious; shy with people; can't make friends; feel lonely; can't make decisions; can't keep a job; inferiority feelings; home conditions bad; financial problems.

3. PERSONAL DATA

Date of birth and place: ....

Mother's condition during pregnancy (as far as you know): ....

Underline any of the following that applied during your childhood:

night terrors; bed-wetting; sleep-walking; thumb-sucking; nail-biting; stammering; fears; happy childhood; unhappy childhood.

Health during childhood?..

List illnesses: ....

....

Health during adolescence? ....

List illnesses: ....

....

What is your height?...................... Your weight?......................

Any surgical operations? (Please list them and give age at time) ....

....

Any accidents? ....

When was the last time you felt well both physically and emotionally for a sustained period? ....

....

Games and interests during childhood (including make-believe): ....

....

Interests and hobbies during adolescence: ....

....

Any athletic accomplishments? ....

....

Present interests, hobbies, activities: ....

....

How is most of your free time occupied? ....

....

Age of beginning school:................. Age of finishing school:...........

Standard reached:............. Relationship to school mates:..............

Scholastic abilities and disabilities: ....

....

Were you ever bullied or given a nickname?..
Do you make friends easily?.............. Do you keep them?..............

4. Occupational Data

Age of starting work:...
Jobs held (in chronological order) and reasons for change: ....
....
....
....
Does your present work satisfy you? (If not, in what ways are you dissatisfied?) ....
....
What do you earn?........... How much does it cost you to live?...........
Ambition(s): ....

5. Sex Information

Parental attitudes to sex (e.g. was there sex instruction or discussion in the home?) ....
....
When and how did you derive your first knowledge of sex? ....
....
When did you first become aware of your own sexual impulses? ....
....
Did you ever experience any anxieties or guilt feelings arising out of sex or masturbation? If "yes", please explain:...
....
Please provide information about any significant heterosexual (and/or homosexual) reactions: ....
....

5a Menstrual History

Age at first period: ....
Are you regular?..............
Duration:.......................
Date of last period: ....

Were you informed or did it come as a shock? ....
Do you have pain? ....
Do your periods affect your moods?........

6. Marital History

How long did you know your marriage partner before engagement?...........
For how long were you engaged? ....
In what areas is there compatibility?.......................
....

Husband's/Wife's age:
,, ,, occupation: ....
,, ,, personality (in your own words): ....
....

In what areas is there incompatibility? ....
....
How do you get along with your in-laws? (this includes brothers and sisters-in-law) ....
....

How many children have you? (Please list them in chronological order with names, ages, sex, personality. State if any children are from a previous marriage. Also list miscarriages, if any): ....
....
....
....
Give details of any previous marriage: ....
....

7. Family Data

(a) *Father*

Name: .... If deceased, cause of death:...........
Age:...................... ....
Occupation:............................... Your age at the time: ....
Health:......................................

(b) *Mother*

Name: .... If deceased, cause of death:...........
Age:...................... ....
Occupation:............................... Your age at the time: ....
Health: ....

(c) *Siblings*

Brothers (names, ages, occupations. Also indicate whether they are single, married, divorced, etc.) ....
....
Sisters (names, ages, occupations. Also indicate whether they are single, married, divorced, etc.): ....
....
Relationship with brothers and sisters:
(a) Past: ....
....
(b) Present: ....
....
Give a description of your father's personality and his attitude towards you (past and present): ....
....
Give a description of your mother's personality and her attitude towards you (past and present): ....
....
In what ways were you punished by your parents as a child?...................
....
Give an impression of your home atmosphere (i.e. the home in which you grew up. Mention state of compatibility between parents and between parents and children): ....
....
Were you able to confide in your parents? ....
If you have a step-parent, give your age when parent re-married:.............
Give an outline of your religious training:...
....

If you were not brought up by your parents, who did bring you up and between what years? ....

....

Has anyone (parents, relatives, friends) ever interfered in your marriage, occupation, etc.? ....

....

Who are the most important people in your life? ....

....

Does any member of your family suffer from alcoholism, epilepsy, or anything which can be considered a "mental disorder"? ....

....

Are there any other members of the family about whom information regarding illness, etc., is relevant? ....

....

Please recount any fearful or distressing experiences not previously mentioned: ....

....

8. SELF-DESCRIPTION

Use the blank sides of these pages to give a word-picture of yourself as would be described:

(a) By your husband/wife.
(b) By your best friend.
(c) By your worst enemy (or someone who dislikes you).
(d) By yourself.

APPENDIX 2

Personality Schedule

Instructions: The questions in this schedule are intended to indicate various emotional personality traits. It is not a test in any sense because there are no right and wrong answers to any of the questions in this schedule.

After each question you will find a row of numbers whose meaning is given below. All you have to do is to draw a ring around the number that describes you best.

0 means "no", "never", "not at all", etc.
1 means "somewhat", "sometimes", "a little", etc.
2 means "about as often as not", "an average amount", etc.
3 means "usually", "a good deal", "rather often", etc.
4 means "practically always", "entirely", etc.

1. Do you get stage fright? 0 1 2 3 4
2. Do you worry over humiliating experiences? 0 1 2 3 4
3. Are you afraid of falling when you are on a high place? 0 1 2 3 4
4. Are your feelings easily hurt? 0 1 2 3 4
5. Do you keep in the background on social occasions? 0 1 2 3 4
6. Are you happy and sad by turns without knowing why? 0 1 2 3 4
7. Are you shy? 0 1 2 3 4
8. Do you day-dream frequently? 0 1 2 3 4
9. Do you get discouraged easily? 0 1 2 3 4
10. Do you say things on the spur of the moment and then regret them? 0 1 2 3 4
11. Do you like to be alone? 0 1 2 3 4
12. Do you cry easily? 0 1 2 3 4
13. Does it bother you to have people watch you work even when you do it well? 0 1 2 3 4
14. Does criticism hurt you badly? 0 1 2 3 4
15. Do you cross the street to avoid meeting someone? 0 1 2 3 4
16. At a reception or tea do you avoid meeting the important person present? 0 1 2 3 4
17. Do you often feel just miserable? 0 1 2 3 4
18. Do you hesitate to volunteer in a class discussion or debate? 0 1 2 3 4
19. Are you often lonely? 0 1 2 3 4
20. Are you self-conscious before superiors? 0 1 2 3 4

21. Do you lack self-confidence? 0 1 2 3 4
22. Are you self-conscious about your appearance? 0 1 2 3 4
23. If you see an accident does something keep you from giving help? 0 1 2 3 4
24. Do you feel inferior? 0 1 2 3 4
25. Is it hard to make up your mind until the time for action is past? 0 1 2 3 4

Your Name: ....
Date:..

APPENDIX 3

Fear Inventory

The items in this questionnaire refer to things and experiences that may cause fear or other unpleasant feelings. Write the number of each item in the column that describes how much you are disturbed by it nowadays.

	Not at all	A little	A fair amount	Much	Very much
1. Noise of vacuum cleaners ..					
2. Open wounds					
3. Being alone					
4. Being in a strange place ..					
5. Loud voices					
6. Dead people					
7. Speaking in public					
8. Crossing streets					
9. People who seem insane ..					
10. Falling					
11. Automobiles					
12. Being teased					
13. Dentists					

	Not at all	A little	A fair amount	Much	Very much
14. Thunder					
15. Sirens					
16. Failure					
17. Entering a room where other people are already seated ..					
18. High places on land					
19. Looking down from high buildings					
20. Worms					
21. Imaginary creatures ..					
22. Receiving injections ..					
23. Strangers					
24. Bats					
25. Journeys by train					
26. Journeys by bus					
27. Journeys by car					
28. Feeling angry					
29. People in authority					
30. Flying insects					
31. Seeing other people injected					
32. Sudden noises					
33. Dull weather					
34. Crowds					

	Not at all	A little	A fair amount	Much	Very much
35. Large open spaces					
36. Cats					
37. One person bullying another					
38. Tough-looking people ..					
39. Birds					
40. Sight of deep water					
41. Being watched working ..					
42. Dead animals					
43. Weapons					
44. Dirt					
45. Crawling insects					
46. Sight of fighting					
47. Ugly people					
48. Fire					
49. Sick people					
50. Dogs					
51. Being criticized					
52. Strange shapes					
53. Being in an elevator ..					
54. Witnessing surgical operations					
55. Angry people					

	Not at all	A little	A fair amount	Much	Very much
56. Mice					
57. Blood					
a—Human					
b—Animal					
58. Parting from friends ..					
59. Enclosed places					
60. Prospect of a surgical operation					
61. Feeling rejected by others ..					
62. Airplanes					
63. Medical odors					
64. Feeling disapproved of ..					
65. Harmless snakes					
66. Cemeteries					
67. Being ignored					
68. Darkness					
69. Premature heart beats (missing a beat)					
70. Nude men (a)					
Nude women (b)					
71. Lightning					
72. Doctors					
73. People with deformities ..					
74. Making mistakes					

	Not at all	A little	A fair amount	Much	Very much
75. Looking foolish					
76. Losing control					

APPENDIX 4

Relaxation Techniques

Relaxation of Arms (time: 4–5 min)

Settle back as comfortably as you can. Let yourself relax to the best of your ability. . . . Now, as you relax like that, clench your right fist, just clench your fist tighter and tighter, and study the tension as you do so. Keep it clenched and feel the tension in your right fist, hand, forearm . . . and now relax. Let the fingers of your right hand become loose, and observe the contrast in your feelings. . . . Now, let yourself go and try to become more relaxed all over. . . . Once more, clench your right fist really tight . . . hold it, and notice the tension again. . . . Now let go, relax; your fingers straighten out, and you notice the difference once more. . . . Now repeat that with your left fist. Clench your left fist while the rest of your body relaxes; clench that fist tighter and feel the tension . . . and now relax. Again enjoy the contrast. . . . Repeat that once more, clench the left fist, tight and tense. . . . Now do the opposite of tension—relax and feel the difference. Continue relaxing like that for a while. . . . Clench both fists tighter and tighter, both fists tense, forearms tense, study the sensations . . . and relax; straighten out your fingers and feel that relaxation. Continue relaxing your hands and forearms more and more. . . . Now bend your elbows and tense your biceps, tense them harder and study the tension feelings . . . all right, straighten out your arms, let them relax and feel that difference again. Let the relaxation develop. . . . Once more, tense your biceps; hold the tension and observe it carefully . . . Straighten the arms and relax; relax to the best of your ability. . . . Each time, pay close attention to your feelings when you tense up and when you relax. Now straighten your arms, straighten them so that you feel most tension in the triceps muscles along the back of your arms; stretch your arms and feel that tension. . . . And now relax. Get your arms back into a comfortable position. Let the relaxation proceed on its own. The arms should feel comfortably heavy as you allow them to relax. . . . Straighten the arms once more so that you feel the tension in the triceps muscles; straighten them. Feel that tension . . . and relax. Now let's concentrate on pure relaxation in the arms without any tension. Get your arms comfortable and let them relax further and further. Continue relaxing your arms ever further. Even when your arms seem fully relaxed, try to go that extra bit further; try to achieve deeper and deeper levels of relaxation.

Relaxation of Facial Area with Neck, Shoulders, and Upper Back (time: 4–5 min)

Let all your muscles go loose and heavy. Just settle back quietly and comfortably. Wrinkle up your forehead now; wrinkle it tighter. . . . And now stop wrinkling your forehead, relax and smoothe it out. Picture the entire forehead and scalp becoming smoother as the relaxation increases. . . . Now frown and crease your brows and study the tension. . . . Let go of the tension again. Smooth out the forehead once more. . . . Now, close your eyes tighter and tighter . . . feel the tension . . . and relax your eyes. Keep your eyes closed, gently, comfortably, and notice the relaxation. . . . Now clench your jaws, bite your teeth together; study the tension throughout the jaws. . . . Relax your jaws now. Let your lips part slightly. . . . Appreciate the relaxation. . . . Now press your tongue hard against the roof of your mouth. Look for the tension. . . . All right, let your tongue return to a comfortable and relaxed position. . . . Now purse your lips, press your lips together tighter and tighter. . . . Relax the lips. Note the contrast between tension and relaxation. Feel the relaxation all over your face, all over your forehead and scalp, eyes, jaws, lips, tongue and throat. The relaxation progresses further and further. . . . Now attend to your neck muscles. Press your head back as far as it can go and feel the tension in the neck; roll it to the right and feel the tension shift; now roll it to the left. Straighten your head and bring it forward, press your chin against your chest. Let your head return to a comfortable position, and study the relaxation. Let the relaxation develop. . . . Shrug your shoulders, right up. Hold the tension. . . . Drop your shoulders and feel the relaxation. Neck and shoulders relaxed. . . . Shrug your shoulders again and move them around. Bring your shoulders up and forward and back. Feel the tension in your shoulders and in your upper back. . . . Drop your shoulders once more and relax. Let the relaxation spread deep into the shoulders, right into your back muscles; relax your neck and throat, and your jaws and other facial areas as the pure relaxation takes over and grows deeper . . . deeper . . . ever deeper.

Relaxation of Chest, Stomach and Lower Back (time: 4–5 min)

Relax your entire body to the best of your ability. Feel that comfortable heaviness that accompanies relaxation. Breathe easily and freely in and out. Notice how the relaxation increases as you exhale . . . as you breathe out just feel that relaxation. . . . Now breathe right in and fill your lungs; inhale deeply and hold your breath. Study the tension. . . . Now exhale, let the walls of your chest grow loose and push the air out automatically. Continue relaxing and breathe freely and gently. Feel the relaxation and enjoy it. . . . With the rest of your body as relaxed as possible, fill your lungs again. Breathe in deeply and hold it again. . . . That's fine, breathe out and appreciate the relief. Just breathe normally. Continue relaxing your chest and let the relaxation spread to your back, shoulders, neck and arms. Merely let go . . . and enjoy the relaxation. Now let's pay attention to your abdominal muscles, your stomach area. Tighten your stomach muscles, make your abdomen hard. Notice the tension. . . . And relax.

Let the muscles loosen and notice the contrast. . . . Once more, press and tighten your stomach muscles. Hold the tension and study it. . . . And relax. Notice the general well-being that comes with relaxing your stomach. . . . Now draw your stomach in, pull the muscles right in and feel the tension this way. . . . Now relax again. Let your stomach out. Continue breathing normally and easily and feel the gentle massaging action all over your chest and stomach. . . . Now pull your stomach in again and hold the tension. . . . Now push out and tense like that; hold the tension . . . once more pull in and feel the tension . . . now relax your stomach fully. Let the tension dissolve as the relaxation grows deeper. Each time you breathe out, notice the rhythmic relaxation both in your lungs and in your stomach. Notice thereby how your chest and your stomach relax more and more. . . . Try and let go of all contractions anywhere in your body. . . . Now direct your attention to your lower back. Arch up your back, make your lower back quite hollow, and feel the tension along your spine . . . and settle down comfortably again relaxing the lower back. . . . Just arch your back up and feel the tensions as you do so. Try to keep the rest of your body as relaxed as possible. Try to localize the tension throughout your lower back area. . . . Relax once more, relaxing further and further. Relax your lower back, relax your upper back, spread the relaxation to your stomach, chest, shoulders, arms and facial area. These parts relaxing further and further and further and ever deeper.

Relaxation of Hips, Thighs and Calves Followed by Complete Body Relaxation

Let go of all tensions and relax. . . . Now flex your buttocks and thighs. Flex your thighs by pressing down your heels as hard as you can. . . . Relax and note the difference. . . . Straighten your knees and flex your thigh muscles again. Hold the tension. . . . Relax your hips and thighs. Allow the relaxation to proceed on its own. . . . Press your feet and toes downwards, away from your face, so that your calf muscles become tense. Study that tension. . . . Relax your feet and calves. . . . This time, bend your feet towards your face so that you feel tension along your shins. Bring your toes right up. . . . Relax again. Keep relaxing for a while. . . . Now let yourself relax further all over. Relax your feet, ankles, calves and shins, knees, thighs, buttocks and hips. Feel the heaviness of your lower body as you relax still further. . . . Now spread the relaxation to your stomach, waist, lower back. Let go more and more. Feel that relaxation all over. Let it proceed to your upper back, chest, shoulders and arms and right to the tips of your fingers. Keep relaxing more and more deeply. Make sure that no tension has crept into your throat; relax your neck and your jaws and all your facial muscles. Keep relaxing your whole body like that for a while. Let yourself relax.

Now you can become twice as relaxed as you are merely by taking in a really deep breath and slowly exhaling. With your eyes closed so that you become less aware of objects and movements around you and thus prevent any surface tensions from developing, breathe in deeply and feel yourself becoming heavier. Take in a long, deep breath and let it out very slowly. . . . Feel how heavy and relaxed you have become.

In a state of perfect relaxation you should feel unwilling to move a single muscle in your body. Think about the effort that would be required to raise your right arm. As you *think* about raising your right arm, see if you can notice any tensions that might have crept into your shoulder and your arm. . . . Now you decide not to lift the arm but to continue relaxing. Observe the relief and the disappearance of the tension. . . .

Just carry on relaxing like that. When you wish to get up, count backwards from four to one. You should then feel fine and refreshed, wide awake and calm.

Bibliography

ABRAHAM, D. (1963) Treatment of encopresis with imipramine, *Amer. J. Psychiat.* **119**:891.

APPEL, J. B. (1961) Punishment in the squirrel monkey *Saimiri sciurea*, *Science* **133**:36.

AYLLON, T. (1963) Intensive treatment of psychotic behaviour by stimulus satiation and food reinforcement, *Behav. Res. Ther.* **1**:53.

BACHRACH, A. J., ERWIN, W. J., and MOHR, J. P. (1965) The control of eating behaviour in an anorexic by operant conditioning techniques. In Ullman, L. and Krasner, L., *Case Studies in Behaviour Modification*, New York, Holt, Rinehart & Winston.

BAIN, J. A. (1928) *Thought Control in Everyday Life*, New York, Funk & Wagnals.

BANDURA, A., LIPSHER, D. H., and MILLER, P. E. (1960) Psychotherapists, approach–avoidance reactions to patients' expressions of hostility, *J. Consult. Psychol.* **24**:1.

BANDURA, A., and WALTERS, R. H. (1963) *Social Learning and Personality Development*, New York, Holt, Rinehart & Winston.

BARBER, T. X. (1960) The necessary and sufficient conditions for hypnotic behaviours, *Amer. J. Clin. Hypnosis* **3**:31.

BARBER, T. X. (1962) Toward a theory of hypnosis: posthypnotic behaviour, *Arch. Gen. Psychiat.* **7**:321.

BARBER, T. X. (1962a) Hypnotic age regression: a critical review, *Psychosom. Med.* **24**:286.

BARBER, T. X. (1964) Hypnotizability, suggestibility, and personality, V, A critical review of research findings, *Psychol. Repts.* **14**:299.

BARBER, T. X., and CALVERLEY, D. S. (1964) Toward a theory of "hypnotic" behaviour, *Arch. Gen. Psychiat.* **10**:209.

BARBER, T. X., and HAHN, K. W. (1964) Experimental studies in hypnotic behaviour: physiologic and subjective effects of imagined pain, *J. Nerv. Ment. Dis.* **139**:416.

BERKUN, M. M. (1957) Factors in the recovery from approach–avoidance conflict, *J. Exp. Psychol.* **54**:65.

BLAKEMORE, C. B. (1965) The application of behaviour therapy to a sexual disorder, in Eysenck, H. J., *Experiments in Behaviour Therapy*, Oxford, Pergamon Press.

BLEWETT, D. B., and CHWELOS, N. (1959) *Handbook for the Therapeutic Use of LSD-25. Individual and Group Procedures*, mimeographed.

BRODY, M. W. (1962) Prognosis and results of psychoanalysis, in Nodine, J. H., and Moyer, J. H., *Psychosomatic Medicine*, Philadelphia, Lea & Febiger.

BURNETT, A., and RYAN, E. (1964) Conditioning techniques in psychotherapy, *Canad. Psychiat. Ass. J.* **9**:140.

CAMPBELL, D., SANDERSON, R. E., and LAVERTY, S. G. (1964) Characteristics of a conditioned response in human subjects during extinction trials following a single traumatic conditioning trial, *J. Abnorm. Soc. Psychol.* **68**:627.

CLARK, D. F. (1963) The treatment of monosymptomatic phobia by systematic desensitization, *Behav. Res. Ther.* **1**:63.

COOPER, J. E. (1963) A study of behaviour therapy, *Lancet* **1**:411.

COSTELLO, C. G. (1964) Lysergic acid diethylamide (LSD-25) and behaviour therapy, *Behav. Res. Ther.* **2**:117.

DAVISON, G. C. (1964) A social learning therapy programme with an autistic child, *Behav. Res. Ther.* **2**:149.

DESTOUNIS, N. (1963) Enuresis and imipramine, *Amer. J. Psychiat.* **119**:893.

DROOBY, A. S. (1964) A reliable truce with enuresis, *Dis. Nerv. Syst.* **25**:97.

DROOBY, A. S. (1965) Personal communication.

DRVOTA, S. (1962) Personal communication.

DUNLAP, K. (1932) *Habits: Their Making and Unmaking*, New York, Liveright.

DWORKIN, S., RAGINSKY, B. B., and BOURNE, W. (1937) Action of anaesthetics and sedatives upon the inhibited nervous system, *Curr. Res. Anaesth.* **16**:238.

ELLIS, A. (1962) *Reason and Emotion in Psychotherapy*, New York, Lyle Stuart.

EYSENCK, H. J. (1952) The effects of psychotherapy: an evaluation, *J. Consult. Psychol.* **16**:319.

EYSENCK, H. J. (1953) *Uses and Abuses of Psychology*, London, Penguin Books.

EYSENCK, H. J. (1960) *Behaviour Therapy and the Neuroses*, Oxford, Pergamon Press.

EYSENCK, H. J. (1965) *Experiments in Behaviour Therapy*, Oxford, Pergamon Press.

FELDMAN, M. P., and MACCULLOCH, M. J. (1965) The application of anticipatory avoidance learning to the treatment of homosexuality. 1. Theory, technique and preliminary results, *Behav. Res. Ther.* **2**:165.

FESTINGER, L. (1964) Behavioural support for opinion change, *Publ. Opin. Quart.* **28**:404.

FRANK, J. D. (1961) *Persuasion and Healing*, New York, Schocken Books.

FRANKL, V. (1960) Paradoxical intention: a logotherapeutic technique, *Amer. J. Psychother.* **14**:520.

FRANKS, C. M. (1961) *Conditioning Techniques in Clinical Practice and Research*, New York, Springer.

FREEMAN, H. L., and KENDRICK, D. C. (1960) A case of cat phobia. Treatment by a method derived from experimental psychology, *Brit. Med. J.* **1**:497.

FREUND, K. (1960) Some problems in the treatment of homosexuality, in Eysenck, H. J., *Behaviour Therapy and the Neuroses*, Oxford, Pergamon Press.

FRY, W. H. (1962) The marital content of an anxiety syndrome, *Family Process* **1**:245.

GELDER, M. G., and MARKS, I. M. (1965) A controlled retrospective study of behaviour therapy in phobia patients, *Brit. J. Psychiat.* (**111**:561.)

GELDER, M. G., MARKS, I. M., SAKINOVSKY, I., and WOLF, H. A. (1964) Behavior Therapy and Psychotherapy for Phobic Disorders, Paper at Sixth International Congress of Psychotherapy, London.

GLOVER, E. (1959) Critical notice, *Brit. J. Med. Psychol.* **32**:68.

GLYNN, J. D., and HARPER, P. (1961) Behaviour therapy in transvestism, *Lancet* **1**:619.

GRAY, J. A. (1964) *Pavlov's Typology*, Oxford, Pergamon Press.

GRINKER, R. R., and SPIEGEL, J. P. (1945) *War Neuroses*, Philadelphia, Blakiston.

GUTHRIE, E. R. (1935) *The Psychology of Human Learning*, New York, Harper.

HAMILTON, D. M., and WALL, J. H. (1941) Hospital treatment of patients with psychoneurotic disorders, *Amer. J. Psychiat.* **98**:551.

HERZBERG, A. (1941) *Active Psychotherapy*, London, Research Books.

HORSLEY, J. S. (1936) Narco-analysis: a new technique in short-cut psychotherapy, *Lancet* **1**:55.

HULL, C. L. (1933) *Hypnosis and Suggestibility*, New York, Appleton–Century.

HULL, C. L. (1943) *Principles of Behaviour*, New York, Appleton–Century.

HUSSAIN, A. (1964) Behavior therapy using hypnosis, In Wolpe, J., Salter, A., and Reyna, L. J., *The Conditioning Therapies*, New York, Holt, Rinehart & Winston.

JACOBSON, E. (1938) *Progressive Relaxation*, Chicago, University of Chicago Press.

JACOBSON, E. (1939) Variation of blood pressure with skeletal muscle tension and relaxation, *Ann. Int. Med.* **12**:1194.

JACOBSON, E. (1940) Variation of pulse rate with skeletal muscle tension and relaxation, *Ann. Int. Med.* **13**:1619.

JACOBSON, E. (1964) *Anxiety and Tension Control*, Philadelphia, Lippincott.

JAMES, B. (1962) Case of homosexuality treated by aversion therapy, *Brit. Med. J.* **1**:768.

JONES, H. G. (1960) Continuation of Yates' treatment of a tiquer, in Eysenck, H. J., *Behaviour Therapy and the Neuroses*, Oxford, Pergamon Press.

JONES, H. G. (1960) The behavioural treatment of enuresis nocturna, in Eysenck, H. J., *Behaviour Therapy and the Neuroses*, Oxford, Pergamon Press.

JONES, M. C. (1924) Elimination of children's fears, *J. Exp. Psychol.* **7**:382.

JONES, M. C. (1924b) A laboratory study of fear. The case of Peter, *J. Genet. Psychol.* **31**:308.

KANTOROVICH, N. V. (1929) An attempt at associative reflex therapy in alcoholism, *Psychol. Abstr.*, No. 4282, 1930.

KELLY, G. A. (1955) *The Psychology of Personal Constructs*, New York, W. W. Norton & Co.

KENNEDY, A. (1960) Chance and design in psychotherapy, *J. Ment. Sci.* **106**:1.

KIMBLE, G. A. (1961) *Hilgard and Marquis' Conditioning and Learning*, New York, Appleton–Century–Crofts.

KNIGHT, R. P. (1941) Evaluation of the results of psychoanalytic therapy, *Amer. J. Psychiat.* **98**:434.

KRASNER, L. (1958) Studies of the conditioning of verbal behaviour, *Psychol. Bull.* **55**:148.

KRASNOGORSKI, N. I. (1925) The conditioned reflexes and children's neuroses, *Amer. J. Dis. Child.* **30**:754.

LANDIS, C. (1937) A statistical evaluation of psychotherapeutic methods, in Hinsie, L., *Concepts and Problems of Psychotherapy*, New York, Columbia University Press.

LANG, P. J. (1964) Experimental studies of desensitization psychotherapy, in Wolpe, J., Salter, A., and Reyna, L. J., *The Conditioning Therapies*, New York, Holt, Rinehart & Winston.

LANG, P. J., and LAZOVIK, A. D. (1963) The experimental desensitization of a phobia, *J. Abnorm. Soc. Psychol.* **66**:519.

LANG, P. J., LAZOVIK, A. D., and REYNOLDS, D. (1965) Desensitization, suggestibility and pseudotherapy, *J. Abnorm. Psychol.* **70**:395.

LA VERNE, A. A. (1953) Rapid coma technique of carbon dioxide inhalation therapy, *Dis. Nerv. Syst.* **14**:141.

LAZARUS, A. A. (1958) New methods in psychotherapy: A case study, *S. Afr. Med. J.* **33**:660.

LAZARUS, A. A. (1960) New Group Techniques in the Treatment of Phobic Conditions, unpublished Ph.D. Thesis, University of the Witwatersrand, Johannesburg.

LAZARUS, A. A. (1960a) The elimination of children's phobias by deconditioning, in Eysenck, H. J., 1960 and 1965.

LAZARUS, A. A. (1961) Group therapy of phobic disorders by systematic desensitization, *J. Abnorm. and Soc. Psychol.* **63**:504.

LAZARUS, A. A. (1963) The results of behaviour therapy in 126 cases of severe neurosis, *Behav. Res. Ther.* **1**:69.

LAZARUS, A. A. (1963) The treatment of chronic frigidity by systematic desensitization, *J. Nerv. Ment. Dis.* **136**:272.

LAZARUS, A. A. (1964) Crucial procedural factors in desensitization therapy, *Behav. Res. Ther.* **2**:65.

LAZARUS, A. A. (1965) Behaviour therapy, incomplete treatment and symptom substitution, *J. Nerv. Ment. Dis.* **140**:80.

LAZARUS, A. A. (1965a) The treatment of a sexually inadequate man, in Ullmann, L. P., and Krasner, L., *Case Studies in Behaviour Modification*, New York, Holt, Rinehart & Winston.

LAZARUS, A. A. (1965b) Towards the understanding and effective treatment of alcoholism, *S. Afr. Med. J.* **39**:736.

LAZARUS, A. A. (1965c) A preliminary report on the use of directed muscular activity in counter-conditioning, *Behav. Res. Ther.* **2**:301.

LAZARUS, A. A., and ABRAMOVITZ, A. (1962) The use of "emotive imagery" in the treatment of children's phobias, *J. Ment. Sci.* **108**:191.

LAZARUS, A. A., DAVISON, G. C., and POLEFKA, D. (1965) Classical and operant factors in the treatment of a school phobia, *J. Abnorm. Psychol.* **70**:225.

LEMERE, F. and VOEGTLIN, W. L. (1950) An evaluation of the aversion treatment of alcoholism, *Quart. J. Stud. Alc.* **11**:199.

LEURET, F. (1846) *Du traitement moral de la folie*, Paris, quoted by Stewart (1961).

LINDSLEY, O. R. (1956) Operant conditioning methods applied to research in chronic schizophrenia, *Psychiat. Res. Rep.* **5**:118.

LITTLE, J. C. and JAMES, B. (1964) Abreaction of conditioned fear after 18 years, *Behav. Res. Ther.* **2**:59.

LONDON, P. (1964) *The Modes and Morals of Psychotherapy*, New York, Holt, Rinehart & Winston.

LOVIBOND, S. H. (1963) The mechanism of conditioning treatment of enuresis, *Behav. Res. Ther.* **1**:17.

MALLESON, N. (1959) Panic and phobia, *Lancet* **1**:225.

MASSERMAN, J. H. (1943) *Behaviour and Neurosis*, Chicago, University of Chicago Press.

MASSERMAN, J. H. (1963) Ethology, comparative biodynamics, and psychoanalytic research, in Scher, J., *Theories of the Mind*, New York, Free Press.

MASSERMAN, J. H., and YUM, K. S. (1946) An analysis of the influence of alcohol on the experimental neuroses in cats, *Psychosom. Med.* **8**:36.

MAX, L. W. (1935) Breaking up a homosexual fixation by the conditioned reaction technique: a case study, *Psychol. Bull.* **32**:734.

MAXWELL, R. D. H., and PATERSON, J. W. (1958) Meprobamate in the treatment of stuttering, *Brit. Med. J.* **1**:873.

MCCONAGHY, N. (1964) A year's experience with nonverbal psychotherapy, *Med. J. Austral.* **1**:831.

MCGUIRE, R. J., and VALLANCE, M. (1964) Aversion therapy by electric shock: a simple technique, *Brit. Med. J.* **1**:151.

MESMER, A. (1779) Quoted by Hull, C. L. (1933).

MEYER, V. (1957) The treatment of two phobic patients on the basis of learning principles, *J. Abnorm. Soc. Psychol.* **58**:259.

MEYER, V. (1963) Paper read at Behaviour Therapy Seminar, University of London.

MILLER, N. E., HUBERT, E., and HAMILTON, J. (1938) Mental and behavioural changes following male hormone treatment of adult castration hypogonadism and psychic impotence, *Proc. Soc. Exp. Biol. Med.* **38**:538.

MILLER, R. E., MURPHY, J. V., and MIRSKY, I. A. (1957) Persistent effects of chlorpromazine on extinction of an avoidance response, *Arch. Neurol. Psychiat.* **78**:526.

MOWRER, O. H. (1960) *Learning Theory and Behaviour*, New York, John Wiley & Sons.

MOWRER, O. H., and VIEK, P. (1948) Experimental analogue of fear from a sense of helplessness, *J. Abnorm. Soc. Psychol.* **43**:193.

MURPHY, I. C. (1964) Extinction of an incapacitating fear of earthworms, *J. Clin. Psychol.* **20**:396.

MURRAY, E. J. (1956) The content-analysis method of studying psychotherapy, *Psychol. Monog.* **70** (13, whole No. 420).

NAPALKOV, A. V., and KARAS, A. Y. (1957) Elimination of pathological conditioned reflex connections in experimental hypertensive states, *Zh. Vyssh. Nerv. Deiat.* **7**:402.

OSGOOD, C. E. (1953) *Method and Theory in Experimental Psychology*, New York, Oxford University Press.

PALMER, H. A. (1944) Military psychiatric casualities, *Lancet* **2**:492.

PAUL, G. L. (1966) *Insight versus Desensitization in Psychotherapy*, Stanford, Stanford University Press.

PAVLOV, I. P. (1927) *Conditioned Reflexes*, trans. by G. V. Anrep, New York, Liveright.

PAVLOV, I. P. (1941) *Conditioned Reflexes and Psychiatry*, trans. by W. H. Gantt, New York, International Publ.

PHILPOTT, W. M. (1964) Personal communication.

POPPER, K. R. (1956) *The Logic of Scientific Discovery*, London, Hutchinson.

POPPER, K. R. (1962) On the sources of knowledge and of ignorance, *Encounter* **19**:42.

RACHMAN, S. (1963) *Critical Essays on Psychoanalysis*, Oxford, Pergamon Press.

RAFI, A. A. (1962) Learning theory and the treatment of tics, *J. Psychosom. Res.* **6**:71.

RAYMOND, M. J. (1956) Case of fetishism treated by aversion therapy, *Brit. Med. J.* **2**:854.

RAZRAN, G. (1961) The observable unconscious and the inferable conscious in current Soviet psychophysiology: interoceptive conditioning and the orienting reflex, *Psychol. Rev.* **68**:81.

REYNA, L. J. (1964) Conditioning therapies, learning theory and research, in WOLPE, J., SALTER, A., and REYNA, L. J. (1964).

ROGERS, J. M. (1960) Operant conditioning in a quasi-therapy setting, *J. Abnorm. Soc. Psychol.* **60**:247.

ROSENTHAL, D. (1955) Changes in some moral values following psychotherapy, *J. Consult. Psychol.* **19**:431.

SALTER, A. (1949) *Conditioned Reflex Therapy*, New York, Creative Age Press; (1961) New York, Capricorn Books–Putnam's Sons.

SALTER, A. (1952) *The Case Against Psychoanalysis*, New York, Holt.

SANDISON, R. A. (1954) Psychological aspects of the LSD treatment of the neuroses, *J. Ment. Sci.* **100**:508.

SARGANT, W., and DALLY, P. (1962) The treatment of anxiety states by antidepressant drugs, *Brit. Med. J.* **1**:6.

SARGANT, W. and SLATER, E. (1947) Treatment by insulin in sub-shock doses, *J. Nerv. Ment. Dis.* **105**:493.

SEITZ, P. F. D. (1953) Dynamically oriented brief psychotherapy: psychocutaneous excoriation syndromes, *Psychosom. Med.* **15**:200.

SEMANS, J. H. (1956) Premature ejaculation, a new approach, *S. Med. J.* **49**:353.

SHORVON, H. J., and SARGANT, W. (1947) Excitatory abreaction: with special reference to its mechanism and the use of ether, *J. Ment. Sci.* **93**:709.

SINGH, H. (1963) Therapeutic use of thioridazine in premature ejaculation, *Amer. J. Psychiat.* **119**:891.

SKINNER, B. F. (1953) *Science and Human Behaviour*, New York, Macmillan.

STAMPFL, T. (1964) Quoted by London (1964).

STEVENS, S. S. (1957) On the psychophysical law, *Psychol. Rev.* **64**:153.

STEVENS, S. S. (1962) The surprising simplicity of sensory metrics, *Amer. Psychol.* **17**:29.

STEWART, M. A. (1961) Psychotherapy by reciprocal inhibition, *Amer. J. Psychiat.* **188**:175.

STONE, D. R. (1955) Responses to imagined auditory stimuli as compared to recorded sounds, *J. Consult. Psychol.* **19**:254.

STORROW, H. A., and SPANNER, M. (1962) Does psychotherapy change patients' attitudes?, *J. Nerv. Ment. Dis.* **134**:440.

TAYLOR, J. G. (1962) *The Behavioural Basis of Perception*, New Haven, Yale University Press.

TAYLOR, J. G. (1963) A behavioural interpretation of obsessive–compulsive neuroses, *Behav. Res. Ther.* **1**:237.

TERHUNE, W. S. (1949) The phobic syndrome, *Arch. Neurol. Psychiat.* **62**:162.

THORPE, J. G., SCHMIDT, E., and CASTELL, D. (1964) A comparison of positive and negative (aversive) conditioning in the treatment of homosexuality, *Behav. Res. Ther.* **1**:357.

ULLMANN, L. P., and KRASNER, L. (1965) *Case Studies in Behaviour Modification*, New York, Holt, Rinehart & Winston.

WALTON, D. (1964) Experimental psychology and the treatment of a ticquer. J. Child. *Psychol. Psychiat* **2**:148.

WATSON, J. B., and RAYNER, P. (1920) Conditioned emotional reactions, *J. Exper. Psychol.* **3**:1.

WEITZENHOFFER, A. M. (1957) *General Techniques of Hypnotism*, New York, Grune & Stratton.

WILDER, J. (1945) Facts and figures on psychotherapy, *J. Clin. Psychopath.* **7**:311.

WILLIAMS, C. D. (1959) The elimination of tantrum behaviour by extinction procedures: case report, *J. Abnorm. Soc. Psychol.* **59**:269.

WILLOUGHBY, R. R. (1934) Norms for the Clark–Thurstone Inventory, *J. Soc. Psychol.* **5**:91.

WINKELMAN, N. W. (1955) Chlorpromazine in the treatment of neuropsychiatric disorders, *J.A.M.A.* **155**:18.

WOHLGEMUTH, A. (1923) *A Critical Examination of Psychoanalysis*, London, Allen & Unwin.

WOLBERG, L. (1948) *Medical Hypnosis*, New York, Grune & Stratton.

WOLPE, J. (1948) An Approach to the Problem of Neurosis Based on the Conditioned Response, unpublished M.D. thesis, University of the Witwatersrand.

WOLPE, J. (1952) Objective psychotherapy of the neuroses, *S. Afr. Med. J.* **26**:825.

WOLPE, J. (1952a) Experimental neurosis as learned behaviour, *Brit. J. Psychol.* **43**:243.

WOLPE, J. (1954) Reciprocal inhibition as the main basis of psychotherapeutic effects, *Arch. Neurol. Psychiat.* **72**:205.

WOLPE, J. (1956) Learning versus lesions as the basis of neurotic behaviour, *Amer. J. Psychiat.* **112**:923.

WOLPE, J. (1958) *Psychotherapy by Reciprocal Inhibition*, Stanford, Stanford University Press.

WOLPE, J. (1961) The systematic desensitization treatment of neuroses, *J. Nerv. Ment. Dis.* **112**:189.

WOLPE, J. (1961a) The prognosis in unpsychoanalysed recovery from neurosis, *Amer. J. Psychiat.* **118**:35.

WOLPE, J. (1962) Isolation of a conditioning procedure as the crucial psychotherapeutic factor, *J. Nerv. Ment. Dis.* **134**:316.

WOLPE, J. (1963) Quantitative relationships in the systematic desensitization of phobias, *Amer. J. Psychiat.* **119**:1062.

WOLPE, J. (1964) Behaviour therapy in complex neurotic states, *Brit. J. Psychiat.* **110**:28.

WOLPE, J. (1965) Conditioned inhibition of craving in drug addiction: a pilot experiment, *Behav. Res. Ther.* **2**:285.

WOLPE, J., and LANG, P. J. (1964) A fear survey schedule for use in behaviour therapy, *Behav. Res. Ther.* **2**:27.

WOLPE, J., and RACHMAN, S. (1960) Psychoanalytic evidence: a critique based on Freud's case of Little Hans, *J. Nerv. Ment. Dis.* **131**:135.

WOLPE, J., SALTER, A., and REYNA, L. J. (1964) *Conditioning Therapies: The Challenge in Psychotherapy*, New York, Holt, Rinehart & Winston.

YATES, A. J. (1958) The application of learning theory to the treatment of tics, *J. Abnorm. Soc. Psychol.* **56**:175.

Author Index

Abraham, D. 117
Abramovitz, A. 143
Appel, J. B. 136, 140
Ayllon, T. 14

Bachrach, A. J. 14
Bain, J. A. 133
Bandura, A. ii, 10
Barber, T. X. 96, 135
Berkun, M. M. 120
Blakemore, C. B. 151
Blewett, D. B. 128
Bourne, W. 119
Burnett, A. 156

Campbell, D. 8, 15, 136
Castell, D. 152
Chwelos, N. 128
Clark, D. F. 59, 77
Cooper, J. E. 159, 160
Costello, C. G. 124, 128

Dally, P. 116
Davison, G. C. 14, 40
Destounis, N. 117
Drooby, A. S. 117
Drvota, S. 59
Dunlap, K. 4, 15, 136
Dworkin, S. 119

Ellis, A. 131
Erwin, W. J. 14
Eysenck, H. J. iii, 7, 113, 154, 155, 157

Feldman, M. P. 152
Festinger, L. 131
Frankl, V. 15, 139
Franks, C. M. 10
Freeman, H. L. 141
Freud, S. 3, 93
Freund, K. 151
Fry, W. H. 93

Gelder, M. G. 159, 160, 161
Glover, E. ii
Glynn, J. D. 151
Gray, J. A. 140
Grinker, R. R. 124, 125
Guthrie, E. R. 4, 139

Hahn, K. W. 96
Hamilton, J. 118
Harper, P. 151
Herzberg, A. 56
Horsley, J. S. 126
Hubert, E. 118
Hull, C. L. ii, 15, 135
Hussain, A. 156

Jacobson, E. 58, 59, 61, 65, 77
James, B. 127, 151
Jones, H. G. 14, 117, 136
Jones, M. C. 7, 55, 145

Kantorovich, N. V. 151
Karas, A. Y. 104
Kelly, G. A. 134
Kendrick, D. C. 141
Kennedy, A. 154
Kimble, G. A. ii
Knight, R. P. 160
Krasner, L. 9, 10
Krasnogorski, N. I. 8

Landis, C. 154
Lang, P. J. 8, 27, 67, 159
LaVerne, A. A. 78, 121

Laverty, S. G. 8, 15, 136
Lazarus, A. A. iii, 40, 84, 85, 102, 142, 143, 146, 152, 153, 155, 156, 157, 158
Lazovik, A. D. 8, 159
Lemere, F. 151
Leuret, F. 2
Lindsley, O. R. 14
Little, J. C. 127
London, P. 10, 22, 139
Lovibond, S. H. 14, 117

MacCulloch, M. J. 152
Malleson, N. 15, 136
Marks, I. M. 159, 160, 161
Masserman, J. H. 5, 119, 136, 140, 156
Max, L. W. 151
Maxwell, R. D. H. 118, 121
McConaghy, N. 156, 157
McGuire, R. J. 151, 152
Meduna, L. J. 121
Mesmer, A. 2
Meyer, V. 95, 141
Miller, N. E. 118
Miller, R. E. 119, 120
Mirsky, I. A. 119, 120
Mohr, J. P. 14
Mowrer, O. H. ii, 146
Murphy, I. C. 141
Murphy, J. V. 119, 120
Murray, E. J. 10

Napalkov, A. V. 104

Osgood, C. 7, 93

Palmer, H. A. 127
Patterson, J. W. 118, 121
Paul, G. iii, 158
Pavlov, I. P. 4, 8, 119, 140, 147
Philpot, W. M. 147
Polefka, D. 40
Popper, K. R. ii
Potter, S. 53

Rachman, S. 157
Rafi, A. A. 136
Raginsky, B. B. 119
Raymond, M. J. 151
Rayner, P. 8
Razran, G. ii
Reade, W. 22
Reyna, L. J. 11
Reynolds, D. 8, 159
Rogers, J. M. 10
Rosenthal, D. 10
Ryan, E. 156

Sakinovsky, I. 159, 160
Salter, A. 38, 44, 48, 51, 57, 157
Sanderson, R. E. 8, 15, 136
Sandison, R. A. 128
Sargant, W. 116, 127, 145
Schmidt, E. 152
Seitz, P. F. D. 48
Semans, J. H. 106
Shorvon, H. J. 127
Singh, J. P. 124, 125
Skinner, B. F. ii, 14
Slater, E. 127, 145
Spanner, M. 48
Spiegel, J. P. 124, 125
Stampfl, T. 139, 140
Stevens, S. S. 89, 90
Stewart, M. A. 2
Stone, D. R. 96
Storrow, H. A. 48

Taylor, J. G. 131, 133
Terhune, W. S. 56
Thorpe, J. G. 152

Ullmann, L. P. 9

Vallance, M. 151, 152
Viek, P. 146
Voegtlin, W. L. 151

Walters, R. H. ii
Walton, D. 136
Watson, J. B. 8
Weitzenhoffer, A. M. 135

Wilder, J. 154
Williams, C. D. 14
Willoughby, R. R. 26
Winkelman, N. W. 120
Wohlgemuth, A. 157
Wolberg, L. 79
Wolff, H. H. 159, 160
Wolpe, J. i, ii, iii, 5, 6, 7, 9, 15, 26, 27, 44, 56, 59, 67, 72, 77, 86, 91, 96, 98, 99, 102, 113, 123, 124, 125, 136, 140, 146, 151, 153, 155, 157

Yates, A. J. 15, 136
Yum, K. S. 119

Subject Index

Abreaction 124–129
  definition 124
  facilitation by drugs 126–129, 137
Alcohol, in therapy of experimental neurosis 119
Alcoholism, aversive therapy and 151–152
Ambivalent stimuli producing neurosis 8
Amphetamine
  abreaction and 127
  anxiety relief conditioning 149
Anorexia nervosa, treatment of 14
Antidepressants, symptomatic use in therapy 116
Anxiety
  alleviation by drugs 116–117
  conditioning as source of human neurosis 6
  "free-floating" 78, 118, 124
  inhibition by assertive responses 13, 39–40
  inhibition by life circumstances 141
  inhibition by motor responses 146
  inhibition by sexual responses 102
  inhibition of, by relaxation 54
  inhibition of, by use of carbon dioxide 123
  muscular paralysis and 8
  pervasive (*q.v.*) 78, 118, 124
  stimulus hierarchies 7, 66–77
"Anxiety-relief" responses 21, 93, 149–151
  combined with aversion therapy 152
Apomorphine in treatment of alcoholism 151
Assertive responses in therapy 38–53
  basic strategy 42–44
  by-product of other therapies 48
  case illustrations 45–46, 48–53
  gathering of strategic information 40–42
  learning mechanisms in 39–40
  training procedures 44–48
Atarax, symptomatic use in therapy 116
Autonomic effects of relaxation 59
Aversion therapy 13, 151–153
  alcoholism and 151
  combined with "anxiety-relief" conditioning 152

Barbiturates in therapy of neurosis 119
Behavior rehearsal in therapy 46
Behavior therapy
  abreaction and 124–129
  approach to patient 16–19
  assertive responses in 38–53
  aversion therapy 151–153
  avoidance conditioning of obsessions 151
  carbon dioxide 121–124
  conditioned motor responses in 146
  conditioning as effective factor 8
  conditioning of anxiety relief responses 149–151
  correcting misconceptions 130–132
  danger of increasing sensitization 15, 82

Behavior therapy—*cont.*
  definition 1
  desensitization based on galvanic shock interference 147–149
  development of scientific behavior therapy 4–9
  distinctive feature of 9
  drugs in 116–121
  exaggerated-role training 134–135
  experimental extinction of motor habits 136
  group desensitization 142
  historical perspective 1–3
  history taking 24–27
  hypnosis and 135
  initial interview 24–27
    example of 29–37
  intensive neurotic response evocation 135–136
  interview induced responses 125
  introductory statement to patient 16–20
  in vivo desensitization 141–142
  Jacobson's differential relaxation 58, 61–66, 177–180
  methods involving concept control 130–135
  moral issues in 20–23
  patient–therapist relationship 9–10, 28–29
  permissiveness of therapist 29
  real life exposure 139
  records of interviews 82–83
  results of 11, 96–101, 112–115, 154–164
  role of suggestion in 2
  selection of techniques 27–29
  sexual responses 102–115
  stimulus flooding techniques 136–140
  systematic desensitization based on relaxation 54–97
  thought stopping 132–134
  use of emotive imagery 143–145
  use of feeding responses 145
  variants of desensitization 140–151
Bernreuter self-sufficiency questionnaire 27
Bromides in therapy of neurosis 119
Bruxism, case of 136

Carbon dioxide–oxygen therapy 78, 93, 118, 121–124
Chlorpromazine
  to enhance relaxation 78
  symptomatic use 116, 119–121
Clark–Thurstone inventory *see* Willoughby Neuroticism Schedule
Codeine
  aid to therapy 121
  to enhance relaxation 78
Compazine, use in therapy 116
Conditioned inhibition
  based on reciprocal inhibition 2, 12, 13
  of anxiety by a conditioned motor response 146
  of anxiety by sexual responses 105
  of anxiety responses by assertive responses 42
  of obsessional and compulsive habits by aversion therapy 13
  thought stopping and 133
Control scene, use in systematic desensitization 80
Counterconditioning 4, 7, 8, 12–13, 40

Demerol, therapy of addiction to 153
Depression 28, 67, 162
Desensitization *see* Systematic desensitization
Dexamyl, use in therapy 116
Diazepam, use in therapy 117
Di-ethyl ether, abreaction and 127
Drug addiction, case of 153
Drugs in therapy of neurosis
  adjuvant use 118
  for specific deconditioning 119–121

Drugs in therapy of neurosis—*cont.*
symptomatic uses 116–118

Electromyogram 77, 92
Emetine in therapy of alcoholism 151
Emotional responses in therapy 78–79
Emotive imagery in therapy of neurosis 143–145
Empathy 28
Encopresis, drugs in therapy of 117
Endogenous stimuli 76
Enovid, use in therapy 113
Enuresis nocturna
conditioning treatment of 14
drugs in therapy of 117
Ergotamine, use in therapy 118
Ethchlorvynol, use in therapy 116
Experimental neurosis *see* Neurosis, experimental
External inhibition 147
Extinction
definition 4, 14
experimental neurosis and 6, 8, 56
human neurosis and 7, 14–16
of motor habits 136
Eysenck Personality Inventory 27

Fear Survey Schedule 27, 67, 172–176
Feeding responses
anxiety inhibiting properties 6
in therapy of experimental neurosis 5, 6, 7
in therapy of human neurosis 7, 55, 145
Fetish, homosexual 151
Fixed role therapy 134
"Free-floating" anxiety *see* Pervasive anxiety
Frigidity 102–103

Galvanic shock in therapy 146–153
Galvanic skin response 77, 92
Generalization
in experimental neurosis 5–6
in human neurosis 7, 18
mediated 7
Group desensitization 142
Guilt 28, 67, 131

Habit
definition 1
neurotic 1
Hierarchies of anxiety stimuli 7, 66–73
dimensions within a single hierarchy 70
examples of 73–77
Homosexuality 151, 152
Hormones, sex hormones in therapy 104, 118
Hunger, role of 55
Hypnosis
abreaction and 126
in therapy 79, 95, 135

Imipramine
encopresis and 117
enuresis and, 117
in therapy of sexual inadequacy 117–118
Impotence 102–103
hormones in therapy of 118
Inhibition *see* Conditioned inhibition, Protective inhibition, Reciprocal inhibition, External inhibition
"Inhibitory personalities" 38
Insight 12, 130
Insulin in therapy of neurosis 145
In vivo desensitization 96, 141–142

Learning
definition 5
hypothesis of neurosis 5–8
Librium, use in therapy 116
Life History Questionnaire 26, 165–169
Lysergic acid, abreaction and 127–129

Massed practice 136
Maudsley Personality Inventory 27

Mediated generalization 7
Meprobamate
to enhance relaxation 78
stuttering and 118, 121
use in therapy 116
Methedrine, abreaction and 127
Misconceptions, correction of 130–132
Motor responses, use of, in therapy 146

Nardil, use in therapy 116, 117
"Negative practice" in elimination of undesirable motor habits 4, 15, 136
Neurosis, experimental
ambivalent stimulation 8
desensitization methods in animals 56–57
drugs and therapy of 119
feeding therapy 5, 6, 57
learning process in 5–6
mechanism of cure 6
stimulus flooding in therapy 140
theories of causation 4–5
therapy of 5, 6, 57
Neurosis, human
anxiety and 12, 17
basic premise about 12
character neurosis 162
due to direct evocation of anxiety 6
experiments on the production of 8
feeding responses in therapy of 55
intensity of anxiety evoked in causative situation 7
learning process in 6–8
Neurotic response evocation, intensive in therapy of neurotic motor responses 136
Nonspecific treatment effects and abreaction 125

Obsessional reactions
aversion conditioning in therapy 151
relation to anxiety 152
thought stopping in therapy of 133
Operant conditioning i, 9, 14
of assertive responses 40, 145
Overlearning 83, 152

Parnate, use in therapy 116
Pentobarbitone, abreaction and 126
Permissiveness of therapist 29
Perseveration of anxiety 84
Personality change 157
Pervasive anxiety
carbon dioxide–oxygen in 78, 118, 121–124, 145
reinduction by specific anxiety stimuli 124
stimuli to 118
treatment of 124
Phenelzine in therapy 117
Phenobarbitone 120
Placebo effects 2
Positive reconditioning 13–14
Primary stimulus generalization 5, 7
Protective inhibition 140
Psychoanalysis 28, 94, 130, 156–158, 159
Psychopath 21, 55
Psychosis 19, 155
Psychotherapeutic relationship 28–29, 125
Pyschotherapy *see* Behavior therapy

Reactive inhibition 6, 15, 136
autonomic responses and 6, 15
Reassurance in therapy 27, 69, 128
Reciprocal inhibition
of anxiety by use of carbon dioxide 123
of anxiety responses by assertive responses 13
of anxiety responses by motor responses 146
of anxiety responses by relaxation 13
of anxiety responses by sexual responses 102

Reciprocal inhibitions—*cont.*
applications in therapy 12–13
between motor and autonomic responses 146
demonstrated in experimental neurosis 6
desensitization by 54–101
evaluation of methods 154–164
by feeding responses 6, 7, 57
in the life situation 38–53, 102–115
mechanism of cure 6
nonspecific treatment effects and 125
response-eliminating mechanism 13
as therapeutic principle 12
Reinforcement, role of drive reduction in 13, 15
Relaxation
autonomic effects of 59
difficulties of 92–93
enhancement by drugs 78, 118
enhancement by imaginal devices 80
Jacobson's method 58
need for objective indicators of 77
systematic desensitization by 54
training 61–66, 177–180
Respiratory responses in therapy 123
Results of therapy ii, iii
controlled studies of outcome 158–160
criteria of therapeutic change 160–162
personality of therapist and iii, 11, 154–164
uncontrolled clinical studies 155–158
using sexual responses 112–115
using systematic desensitization 96–101
Role training, exaggerated, in therapy 134–135

Secondary generalization 7
Sedatives 119
Selfconcept, changed as result of therapy 47–48
Sensory interference technique 93
Sexual inadequacy
cases of 103–104
choice of strategies in therapy of 28, 102–103
drugs in therapy of 117–118
results of treatments of 112–115
therapy of 104–111
Sexual responses
autonomic effects 104
inhibited by anxiety 104
use in therapy 102–115
Shock apparatus, portable 152
Spontaneous recovery 83
Spontaneous therapy 55
Stelazine, use of, in therapy 116
Stimulus flooding 15, 126, 136–140
examples of 137–139
need to exercise caution in use of 140
Stimulus hierarchies
in animals 56
in humans 66–77
misleading or irrelevant hierarchies 93–95
Stuttering 27
drugs and 118, 121
"negative practice" in therapy of 136
Subjective anxiety scale in therapy 73, 92
"Sud" (subjective unit of disturbance) 73, 122
Suggestion 2
Summation effect 55–56
Support in therapy 27
"Symbolic" reactions 93
case of 94
Symptom substitution ii, 152, 157
Systematic desensitization 54–101
abreaction as adjuvant 124
based on galvanic shock interference 147–149
danger of strong stimuli 15, 82
definition 54

Systematic desensitization—*cont.*
  effective process in 8, 59
  first session 79–83
  formal basis of 56–59
  group 142
  hierarchy construction 66–73
  examples of 73–77
  hypnosis and 79
  in vivo 96
  paradigm of 59–61
  principle of 59–60
  procedure 77–83
  quantitative considerations in 83–91
  results of 96–101
  snags and pitfalls in 91–96
  technique 61–73
  training in relaxation 61–66
  transcription of sessions 82–83
  use of control scene in 80–81
  use of signal in 82
  variants of 140–151
  varying the hierarchy items 81

Testosterone to augment low sexual drive 118
Therapy *see* Behavior therapy
Therapy of experimental neurosis 5, 6
Thought-stopping 69, 132–133
Tics, therapy of 15, 136
Tranquilizers, symptomatic use in therapy 117, 118
Transmarginal inhibition 140
Transvestism 151

Values, change in, during therapy 10

Willoughby Neuroticism Schedule 26–27, 170–171